THROUGH THE EYES OF FAITH

CREATION AND EVOLUTION

Your Word, Lord,
stands forever; it is firm
as the heavens. Through all
generations, Your truth endures;
fixed to stand like the earth.
(Psalm 119:89-90)
Bill

THROUGH THE EYES OF FAITH

CREATION AND EVOLUTION

"What Do We Tell Our Children?"

WILLIAM R. LYNN

ILLUSTRATED BY MICHELE GIANNETTI

Oxen of the Sun Coral Gables

Published by Oxen Of The Sun

CREATION AND EVOLUTION: THROUGH THE EYES OF FAITH

Cover illustrated by Michele Giannetti, designed by Oxen Of The Sun, Inc. © 2014
Illustration on backcover is an uncredited image from a 13th Century manuscript.

Produced in the United States
ISBN 978-0-9829752-9-9 (Paperback)
ISBN 978-0-9829752-8-2 (Hardback)

Oxen Of The Sun, Inc.,
1825 Ponce De Leon Blvd. #289
Coral Gables, FL 33134
oxenofthesun.com

CONTENTS

INTRODUCTION

About Me

I am a former Army officer educated at the United States Military Academy. I spent eight years active duty as an Air Defense Artillery officer with tours of duty in Germany, Vietnam, and in a project management office at the United States Army Missile Command. After active duty, I continued to work as a civilian engineer at the United States Army Missile Command. I also worked as an engineer and senior manager for civilian companies. During my career, I had the opportunity to travel to many countries throughout the world and experience numerous different religions and cultures including five years working in Saudi Arabia.

I grew up in a nominally Christian family. I recall attending Church services occasionally, mostly at a Baptist Church, but never on a regular basis. When I got older, both of my sisters became much more consistent in attending church services. One sister went to a Presbyterian Church; the other went to an Episcopalian Church. I usually went with one or the other of my sisters. As I grew up, especially in high school, I became attracted to the Catholic faith primarily because of the faithfulness of a few Catholic individuals I knew. One such person was later to become my wife. I was impressed by her staunchly held, knowledgeable beliefs. She, and her family, knew what they believed and why they believed it. That was much more than I could say for myself.

Another strong influence on my decision to

become a Catholic was a junior high and high school friend named John Burroughs. We were both in the same Boy Scout Troop and I can clearly remember him on camping trips. On Sunday morning, he would dress up in his scout uniform and the scoutmaster would take him to the nearest Catholic Church. I was so impressed by the fact that he would take time out of the fun of a camping trip to attend to his faith. He was one of the great influences in my life. Unfortunately, I have not seen him since high school and, unless he happens to read this book, he will probably never know what an impact he had on me.

I converted to Catholicism my first year as a West Point cadet. I had taken a correspondence course in the Catholic faith through the Knights of Columbus while I was in high school. As a new cadet at West Point one of the questions we all had to answer was, "What is our religion?" In those days, attendance at Sunday chapel services was mandatory for all cadets. When asked that question, I answered Catholic, and so became one. After spending time with the pastor of the Catholic Chapel receiving instruction in the faith, I was baptized and became officially Catholic.

As a young Army officer, I began earnestly studying the Bible, not just reading it, through several different Bible study groups. As one might expect, my experience studying the Bible over these years has significantly deepened my faith. It has also greatly strengthened my belief and acceptance of the teachings of the Catholic Church. Over the course of these years of study, I can confidently state that I have never encountered any reading of the Bible that I believed contradicted a teaching of the Catholic Church. There have been instances where interpretations of a particular passage of the Bible could plausibly have been contrary to Church teachings, but not so conclusively that I could conclude that the Church was even possibly in error.

This is an important aspect of my approach to this book. I do not think there is anything espoused in this book intentionally contrary to any teaching of the Church. If such an inference can be made, it can only be because my exposition of the issue was inadequate or in error. One of the major references I have used throughout this book is *The Catechism of the Catholic Church*. I have diligently tried to keep everything stated as a belief in this book consistent with the teachings of the Catholic Church as defined in *The Catechism of the Catholic Church*.

As an engineer, one of my major roles has simply been the resolution of problems occurring with electronic systems. The process of resolving engineering problems involves applying many of the principles of scientific research. The problem must be defined. The available data must be analyzed and a possible hypothesis for the cause of the problem must be formulated. If the available data do not support the hypothesis in every aspect, the hypothesis must be discarded or revised. Often, the available data is inadequate to unequivocally verify the hypothesis. In that case, specific tests must be performed to expand the available data. The results of these measurements may cause the hypothesis to again be modified or discarded. Ultimately, the decision must come down to a best judgment about the actions to be taken to correct the problem. But, even that may cause the hypothesis to be subsequently invalidated and again revised.

These two aspects of engineering and faith are used in this book to combine the information available from the Scriptures and the teachings of the Church to form hypotheses about many aspects of Creation and evolution presented by the scientific world. In each case, the hypothesis may be revised or discarded as new scientific information is discovered or my understanding of the Bible and the teachings of the Church grow. It is actually much easier to handle the faith side of the question because our faith is very well defined even if many things remain a mystery beyond our understanding. We are greatly blessed in our age that the Bible is available to us in many translations. Not only do we have the Bible, we have many tools such as concordances, commentaries, and even online Bibles. We are also blessed to have such well-defined teachings of the Church available and well documented in *The Catechism of the Catholic Church*, which is available online with a concordance and search tools. I mention these as a blessing because many of our forefathers in faith did not have such a wealth of information available at their fingertips.

In the early days of the Church, none of this was available. The Old Testament was handed down orally until it began to be written down in about 900 BC. By the time of Our Lord, the Jews possessed written copies of the Old Testament books.[1]

The New Testament was initially transmitted orally as preached by the Disciples of Christ, first to Jewish and then to Gentile communities. The first books of the New Testament were personal letters by St. Paul to individual churches he had founded. Later, the Gospels and other books and letters of the New Testament were written down, forming a completed New Testament by 100 AD.[2] The Bible was put into print with the Gutenberg Bible in the 15th Century. This compact history of the Bible is presented as a prelude to a number of hypotheses and conclusions I will reach in my vision of Creation and evolution seen "through the eyes of faith.

Figure 1 The Gutenberg Bible

Why I Wrote the Book — Adele

I regularly attend a Bible Study program at our Church. One morning, a lady named Adele at my discussion table voiced a concern. Her child had just received a lecture at her public school about evolution and creation. It was all science with no room for any concept of Divine Creation and she was at a loss about what to tell her child. All her religious upbringing was dismissed as a fairy tale.

I spent some time pondering this problem and came to the following conclusion: If the Bible is true, and I believe it is, and the scientific descriptions of the creation and the development of man are true to the extent of verifiable hypotheses, and I believe they are; then the logical conclusion must be that both are true and both are telling the same story from different viewpoints. The problem, then, was how to resolve the viewpoints of the same truth.

The more I investigated the story of Genesis in the Bible and the scientific descriptions of Creation and evolution, the more convinced I became that the similarities were more than just coincidence. I became convinced that, in fact, our God wants us to use our reason to discover this world in a rigorously scientific way, but also to look at the wonders science reveals to us, the wonders of His Creation, "through the eyes of faith" as a way of deepening our faith in Him. As an engineer and scientist, this has always been my response to scientific discovery. I have yet to learn of an advance in scientific knowledge in any field that did not increase my faith in the wonder and majesty of our God.

Thus, the principle aim of this book has been to help people like Adele, to look at scientific discoveries and teachings in secular institutions "through the eyes of faith" without fear of undermining their religious upbringing. It is my hope that this book will be a tool to assist the Adeles of this world to be able to sit down with their children and explain to them that this world we live in is the world God created. It is a world described by science in an objective way. Everything must be testable and measurable. But, it is the same world described by our faith. The more we understand of this world, the more we will understand of our Creator. The wonders of science should lead us to greater awe and wonder of our God. Faith and scientific discovery need not be in conflict. The two dimensional world of a scientific paper becomes filled out in a three dimensional universe, involving real people and real events living in ways that proclaim the theological and moral truths our God wants us to learn and understand.

These differences in focus, events, and Divine truth, go a long way toward understanding the differences we see between science and faith. "St. Thomas Aquinas tells us there are two ways of discovering the existence of God—one, through reason, the inner light by means of which a person acquires knowledge; the other through certain external pointers to the wisdom of God, that is, created things perceivable through the senses: these things are like a book on which are imprinted traces of God."[3] My goal is to make explicit correlations between knowledge accumulated by human reason through science, and the wisdom of God expressed in the Bible so that we may recognize the imprint of the hand of our Creator in processes of life and all of Creation.

What this Book is not About

However much I would like it to be, the purpose of this book is not to bring un-believers to faith. Indeed, the very title of the book presupposes that the reader is a person of faith. My goal is to help that person of faith to endure the constant attacks against faith where those attacks are based on scientific discoveries. My goal is to strengthen that faith so that scientific discovery itself, rather than challenging our beliefs, further increases our faith. After all, we are looking at the same world. Through the eyes of science or "through the eyes of faith," we see the same things. Although, I believe that we can see far more "through the eyes of faith" because we are not bound as science is to hold as truth only what we can verify through objective observation and measurement.

This premise may lead one to jump to the conclusion that I have modified my belief in what the Church teaches to accommodate the latest scientific discovery. I do not believe this conclusion can reasonably be sustained by the contents of this book. Over the years, especially in my contacts with people of other religions, I find that, while tolerant of others' beliefs, I have become less willing to compromise my belief in the tenants of faith and the teachings of the Church to find an area of agreement. Simply put, I am perfectly content for you to believe what you believe, but I have no inclination to modify my beliefs to accommodate yours, and that includes science.

Where science can support a hypothesis, I accept it, but without it changing my religious faith. When looking at scientific discoveries "through the eyes of faith" it is important to understand that science is mostly concerned with processes—e.g. the process of Creation or the process of the development of man. Faith, on the other hand, is mostly concerned with God's relationship with man. Where the processes advance one's faith, it is useful. Where the process does not advance faith, it may be laid aside until science advances or our understanding of the relationship of faith to the process is more complete.

Random Events

One additional point: the rationalization of miraculous events in the Bible to natural phenomena may be, and often is, unrelated to any action by God. In fact, I will insist the contrary is true. Every miracle in the Bible is a direct action of God regardless of any accompanying natural phenomenon.

I am convinced that there are no random events in the natural world other than the decisions of humanity and, only then, because God gave free will to man when He breathed into Adam the breath of His Spirit. A bird sitting in a tree suddenly flits to the ground to gobble up some hapless grasshopper. The bird is merely reacting to a stimulus of the movement of the grasshopper, which its instinct tells it that the grasshopper is a meal. There is nothing random about it. Whereas, a man looking at the same grasshopper may decide, depending on his mood, to bend down and pick up the grasshopper; or, he may decide not to. That is simply a free will choice made by a man.

Consider Haley's comet. Every 77 years it swings in its orbit around the Sun and becomes visible here on Earth. This is not a random event. It is predicable. Scientists readily predict exactly when it will make its next appearance. It is simply following the laws of physics, obeying the Universal Law of Gravitation. But, then so does every other body in the universe. All of these laws were established at the instant of Creation, or soon after, by God and every atom, every burst of energy, every physical entity in the universe has been obeying those Laws ever since.

Let's look at a miracle in the Bible. Take, for example, the Israelites crossing the Red Sea in the Book of Exodus, depicted in Figure 2. Either it is a miracle in which God stepped into human history, subverted the laws of nature which He Himself established and parted the water; or it was merely a natural phenomenon which Moses was able to take advantage of and lead the Israelites safely across. If it was the direct intervention of God at that moment, which I certainly believe God has the power to do, it was a miracle. However, I believe it would be no less miraculous if, at the instant of Creation, God had arranged the energy of the Big Bang precisely so that some 14.5 billion years later, at the very instant of need, the Red Sea would part to allow the Israelites to pass in safety and then, some time later, come crushing down on the pursuing Egyptians:

> **Then Moses stretched out his hand over the sea, and the LORD swept the sea with a strong east wind throughout the night and so turned it into dry land. When the water was thus divided, the Israelites marched into the midst of the sea on dry land, with the water like a wall to their**

right and to their left.
Exodus 14:21-22.

Note that the sea is parted by a "strong east wind throughout the night." This is not quite the vision we have from the classic movie, *The Ten Commandments*, but it shows the hand of God at work through the power of nature. Remember, nothing in nature is random. Every action is caused in reaction to a previous action, and the first action of all, the one "unmoved mover"[4], was God at the instant of the Big Bang: Creation.

Figure 2 Strong east wind parting the Red Sea

THROUGH THE EYES OF FAITH

"Through the eyes of faith" is a phrase used consistently throughout this book. It is the major theme of the book. Simply put, it means looking at the world around us with a sense of the Holy Scriptures and using the teachings of the Church to guide us as we interpret what we see. When we look at the Creation event, typically called the Big Bang, we can read all of the scientific descriptions and explanations of how the events of Creation proceeded. We can also look at those events and descriptions "through the eyes of faith" to get a better understanding of how those same events and descriptions describe the very same things that are presented in the Bible. In the Bible, the descriptions may be more poetically or artistically presented, but the conclusions and the event are clearly the same. In each case, there will be sense of wonder of how the Biblical authors could possibly have known or understood what they were describing. Indeed, this questioning will be rhetorically raised throughout this book. In each case, the answer will be the same—they were inspired by God to describe, as best they could from the world they knew, some momentous event in the formation of the universe or formation of man which they could not have possibly known in any other way.

Over the years of studying the Bible, and especially as I began to assemble this book, I have become convinced that God in His wisdom has deliberately laid out a path of discovery, which we have barely begun to embark upon, that will increase our faith step by step. As each new startling discovery is revealed, looking "through the eyes of faith" will reveal something God has already laid before us, waiting for that discovery that would open our eyes once more to His revealed truth. Indeed, I have become convinced that God has a very well developed sense of humor. That should not strike us as strange because man alone among all the animals has a sense of humor. I think it is most likely that when God breathed His Spirit into Adam, one of the characteristics of God that Adam received was a sense of humor.

My son, reading an early draft of this book, challenged me on this point. He showed me a video he had seen in medical school of a chimpanzee doing a bit crude bathroom humor and then falling out of a tree. The medical students in his class and the band of chimpanzees erupted in a raucous display of laughter. I am not sure if this proved that chimpanzees have a sense of humor or that our poor, bedraggled medical students have the sense of humor of chimpanzees. Since the jury is still out on that, I will stick with my point.

Allow me to offer an example that, in my mind, reveals both the path of discovery God has laid before us and His sense of humor. In his letter to the Colossians, St. Paul says:

> **For in him were created all things in heaven and on earth, the visible and the invisible, whether thrones or dominions or principalities or powers; all things were created through him and for him. He is before all things, and in him all things hold together.**

Colossians 1:16-17.

In the bodies of animals is a protein called laminin. The function of this protein is to hold the cells of the body together. In an article in *Science Daily* laminin was described as follows:

> Like a plug and a socket, a nerve and a muscle fiber mesh at the neuromuscular junction. New work reveals that an extracellular matrix protein called laminin shapes both sides of the junction to ensure they fit together.[5]

I recognize this is technical language, but it makes St. Paul's point and mine. When I look at this particular protein molecule under an electron microscope, a device beyond my scope of comprehension and all the more beyond St. Paul's, it is as if God in His wisdom, and with a wisp of whimsy, deliberately shaped the protein that holds all living things together. A man of faith looking through the electron microscope thousands of years later would see, "through the eyes of faith," and as we see in Figure 3, a protean in the shape of a cross—a symbol so unmistakable and universal a man of faith could not help but see confirmation of the words of St. Paul. Of course, the secular man may see no such thing, but this book is not for him.

St. Thomas Aquinas, in his commentary on St. Paul's First Letter to the Corinthians,

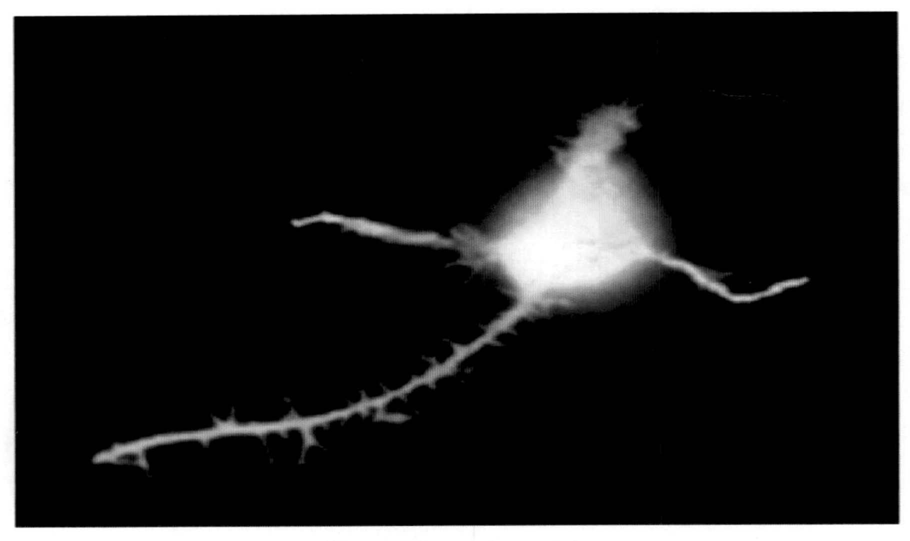

Figure 3 Laminin protein

presents an interesting and somewhat amusing description of the differences between a spiritual man and an unspiritual man by comparing them to one who is awake and one who is asleep.

> A conscious person rightly perceives both that he is awake and the other person is asleep; but the person who is asleep cannot form a correct judgment concerning either himself or the one who is awake. Therefore, things are not the way they are seen by someone asleep: they are as they appear to a conscious person [...]. And so the Apostle says that "the spiritual man judges all things": for a person whose understanding is enlightened and whose affections are regulated by the Holy Spirit forms correct judgments on particular matters to do with salvation. He who is unspiritual has a darkened understanding and disordered affection as far as spiritual things are concerned, therefore the spiritual man cannot be judged by the unspiritual man, just as the sleeping person cannot judge the one who is awake. [6]

I humbly invoke the judgment of St. Thomas Aquinas. I am speaking to the spiritual man who can see "through the eyes of faith" and make judgments regarding spiritual matters. I am not, however, speaking to the unspiritual man, who, like the "one asleep," cannot see the true world around him and therefore cannot make judgments on spiritual matters. He can make secular judgments, but unless he becomes a spiritual man and sees "through the eyes of faith," he cannot understand what this book is about. It is simply not for him.

Example of the Eucharist

I believe that the very best example of looking at things "through the eyes of faith" is the Eucharist. As a Catholic, I firmly believe the Church's teaching that in the Eucharistic celebration of the Mass, our offerings of bread and wine are physically changed into the body and blood of Christ. Although, not detectible by our normal senses, I believe that Christ is truly present: body, blood, soul, and divinity.

I believe this first of all because this is the teaching of the Church handed down from Christ Himself through the apostles and their successors, faithfully keeping this sacred truth under the guidance of the Holy Spirit. I find it particularly significant that the very first description of the Eucharistic event was not written in any of the Gospels, which were written later, but in a letter written by St. Paul, his first letter to the Corinthians written about 56 AD.[7]

> **For I received from the Lord what I also handed on to you, that the Lord Jesus, on the night he was handed over, took bread, and, after he had given thanks, broke it and said, "This is my body that is for you. Do this in remembrance of me." In the same way also the cup, after supper, saying, "This cup is the new covenant in my blood. Do this, as often as you drink it, in remembrance of me." For as often as you eat this bread and drink the cup, you proclaim the death of the Lord until he comes. Therefore whoever eats the bread or drinks the cup of the Lord unworthily will have to answer for the body and blood of the Lord.**

1 Corinthians 17:23-27.

This passage has a significant impact on my understanding of the Eucharist for a number of reasons. First is St. Paul's source. He received this information directly from the Risen Lord. He is even more emphatic about his source in his opening line in the letter to the Galatians.

> **Paul, an apostle not from human beings nor through a human being but through Jesus Christ and God the Father who raised him from the dead.**

Galatians 1:1.

These two passages tell me of the importance of the Eucharist. It was important enough to Our Lord that when He called St. Paul to be His Apostle to the Gentiles, one of the tenants of faith that He passed on to St. Paul was the Eucharist.

I believe this teaching of the Church to be the truth because I have researched the teaching of the Church, exploring the references cited in Catholic apologetics, and I have reached my own conclusion reaffirming my belief in this essential teaching of the Church. I reached this conclusion before I made the commitment to become a member of the Catholic Church. When Our Lord was asked which was the greatest commandment, St. Matthew's Gospel records that He gave this response:

> **You shall love the Lord, your God, with all your heart, with all your soul, and with all your mind. This is the greatest and the first commandment.**

Matthew 22:37-38.

I believe that God wants us to use our minds, our intelligence, and our reason to discover Him and to come closer to Him. There are many things in our religion that we must simply accept on faith, because, there is no way to objectively prove them. However, there is significant supporting evidence and it is our obligation to apply our minds to make those discernments. So it is with my belief in the Eucharist exactly as taught by our Church. I accept it completely on faith, but my reason fully supports my faith. My reasoning goes as follows:

I ask the question, "Does God, Who created from nothing the entire universe, from the largest galaxy to the tiniest subatomic particle, Who holds all things together by His will through the exercise of natural laws which He set into motion at the beginning of time; does this Almighty God have the power, should it please Him to do so, to change bread and wine into Christ Himself, fully present: body, blood, soul, and divinity? The answer to the question from any person of faith would be, "Of course, He can."

The *Catechism of the Catholic Church* affirms this conclusion.

> 268 Of all the divine attributes, only God's omnipotence is named in the Creed: To confess this power has great bearing on our lives. We believe that his might is universal, for God who created everything also rules everything and can do everything. [8]

Given an affirmative answer to the question, I then look to the Holy Scriptures in St. Matthew's Gospel where Our Lord says:

> **Again, (amen,) I say to you, if two of you agree on earth about anything for which they are to pray, it shall be granted to them by my heavenly Father. For where two or three are gathered together in my name, there am I in the midst of them."**

Matthew 20:19-20.

Or, look again in St. John's Gospel where Our Lord was talking to His Apostles, those upon whom His Church would be built and who would pass down their Apostolic Authority through what the Church refers to as Apostolic Succession, where Our Lord says:

> **Amen, amen, I say to you, whoever believes in me will do the works that**

I do, and will do greater ones than these, because I am going to the Father. And whatever you ask in my name, I will do, so that the Father may be glorified in the Son. If you ask anything of me in my name, I will do it.

John 14:12-14.

This, then, leads to the conclusion that when devout Catholics come together to celebrate the Holy Mass, agreeing and joining the priest and each other in the unity of prayer, asking:

> "Be pleased, O God, we pray, to bless, acknowledge, and approve this offering in every respect; make it spiritual and acceptable, so that it may become for us the Body and Blood of your most beloved Son, our Lord Jesus Christ."[9]

In honor of His promise, God will make it so.

Following the repetition of Our Lord's words of consecration that He uttered at the Last Supper, the priest elevates the sacred host and chalice in turn. At this point, we come to the crescendo of "seeing through the eyes of faith." As a believing, faithful Catholic, I see in the hands of the priest the presence of My Lord and Savior: Body, Blood, Soul, and Divinity.

I offer my prayer of faith and praise beginning with the words of St. Thomas at his encounter with the Risen Lord in the upper room, "My Lord and My God!" John 20:28.

I ask Him to strengthen me against temptation and sin: "Lord, may this, Your most precious body and blood strengthen me against temptation and sin."

And I heed the admonition of St. Paul: "For anyone who eats and drinks without discerning the body, eats and drinks judgment on himself," 1 Corinthians 11:29.

I pray that I may be able to discern His presence not only in the host and chalice; I ask, "Lord Jesus, help me recognize in Your people, Your most precious Body."

How can I be certain of the complete presence of Christ in the Holy Eucharist: Body and Blood, Soul and Divinity?

My senses do not tell me this. My senses tell me it is still bread and wine.

In the thirteenth century, St. Thomas Aquinas captured this thought in the hymn, *Tantum Ergo*, celebrating our belief in the bread and wine becoming truly Jesus Christ. Translated from the Latin, this hymn, which is still sung to this day, says in part, "Faith for all defects supplying, where the feeble senses fail."

Scientific analysis will not confirm this transformation. Without doubt, the Holy Eucharist will still have all the properties of bread and wine and none of the properties of human flesh and blood, still less the ineffable qualities of the soul and divinity of Christ. A detailed analysis of the chemical properties and DNA will show nothing of human flesh and blood. It would show only the ingredients of bread and the properties of wine.

Certainly, the world outside the faithful

remnant will see and adamantly tell me it is still merely bread and wine. Indeed, there are those who write books, live the lives of celebrities, and are frequent guests of media commentaries insisting that any belief or faith in God is merely a delusion.

Yet, still, "through my eyes of faith," My Lord is present, and when I consume this Holy Food come down from heaven, Christ becomes a part of me in every possible sense: physical, spiritual, intellectual. In addition, I become a part of Him. I am united with believing Catholics throughout the world as part of the Body of Christ, the Church, and I mean the Church in the broadest sense of all Christian believers. As a part of Him, I recognize my obligation before God to love as He has loved us and to seek out the poor and needy of the world to offer what help I can. I can assure you that this latter is not a part of my comfort zone. Mother Teresa was apparently quite comfortable among the poor and needy. I am very uncomfortable there.

Now, one may reasonably ask why God, who has established all these laws of the universe to keep things moving in an orderly and predictable fashion, would violate an untold number of these laws to satisfy this ancient and unique practice. Of course, you can ask this of any answer to prayer or miraculous event. However, the Eucharistic mystery, uniquely and on a regular basis, occurs on demand in the celebration of the Holy Mass every day throughout the world before millions of people.

The Church has provided numerous answers which are more eloquent and more comprehensive than any I can provide. They are described in the *Catechism of the Catholic Church* in the description of the Sacraments.

In addition, I think there is one reason that is particularly apropos to the central theme of this book. That is that the celebration of the Eucharist gives the believing Catholic, on a weekly basis or even on a daily basis, practice in "seeing through the eyes of faith." Every time we go to Mass and partake of the Eucharist, we are practicing by repetition our trust in the Word of God and eschewing the "wisdom" of the world.

For all the reasons I described and many more, it simply cannot be; yet, "seen through the eyes of faith" it is true, because Our Lord has told us it is true.

> **"This is my body which is given for you. Do this in remembrance of Me.... This cup which is poured out for you is the new covenant in my blood."**

Luke 22:19-20.

I think that Our Lord gave His disciples one more clue to this miraculous event when, as recorded in the Gospel of St. Matthew, He told them:

> **I tell you, you will not see me again until you say, "Blessed is he who comes in the name of the Lord."**

Matthew 23:39.

After Our Lord's Passion, Resurrection, and Ascension; the Church, led by the Holy Spirit, began to memorialize these events in a weekly celebration of the breaking of the bread, the Eucharist.

> **On the first day of the week when we gathered to break bread...**

Acts 20:7.

When the Church Fathers established the order of the Mass, I'm sure it was not by accident that they included the acclamation recorded in all four Gospels:

> **Blessed is he who comes in the name of the Lord!**

Matthew 21:9; Mark 11:9; Luke 19:38; John 12:13.

This acclamation is immediately followed by the Consecration when we, indeed, behold again Our Lord and Savior Jesus Christ, now seen in the form of bread and wine, but not through our physical senses. "Through the eyes of faith," we see that bread and wine transformed by His power, transubstantiated, to use the theological term, into Jesus Christ: Body, Blood, Soul, and Divinity.

I believe that this is precisely what He meant when He taught his disciples how to pray: "Give us this day our daily bread." Certainly, He meant the ordinary food we need to sustain life just as every other living creature needs its daily bread. But, unlike any other living thing in the world, human beings have been given a spiritual life, breathed into them by God at the creation of the human species. This spiritual life can only be sustained by our faith in God. Thus, in the Lord's Prayer, we also ask for the daily bread that comes down from heaven, the very Person of Jesus Christ; Body, Blood, Soul, and Divinity; which we receive in the Eucharist. As Our Lord said:

> **For my flesh is true food, and my blood is true drink. Whoever eats my flesh and drinks my blood remains in me and I in him. Just as the living Father sent me and I have life because of the Father, so also the one who feeds on me will have life because of me. This is the bread that came down from heaven. Unlike your ancestors who ate and still died, whoever eats this bread will live forever.**

John 6:55-58.

When we look at the Eucharist "through the eyes of faith," we see not the elements of bread and wine, rather we see the Presence of Christ Himself. As we look at various physical phenomena from the Creation of the universe at the Big Bang, to the advent of life, through the evolution of man; "seeing through eyes of faith" will give us a more complete view of the world around us.

But, more importantly, we can see, rather than conflicts between science and faith, harmony and confirmation of our faith in God.

I am fully convinced that the more we learn about our world and our universe, the more certain we will become in the truth of our faith in God.

Prayer

I will tell you that the writing of this book has been accomplished with much prayer. I will also tell you that prayer is one of those mysteries of the faith that I absolutely cannot grasp. Not that I do not believe in prayer, I most emphatically do; it is that I cannot understand it. This is particularly true when we pray for someone else. To me it makes no sense that anything I may say will influence God (that in itself seems patently absurd) to change His mind, alter His will, or change the laws of nature which He set into motion from the beginning of Creation to satisfy some request that I may make. But I have seen the power of prayer at work in my life and in the life of my wife, Patty, in ways that have been overwhelming and humbling.

In the summer of 2013 my beloved wife of forty six years was diagnosed with inoperable stage four lung cancer. My wife is a lifelong non-smoker so this came as quite a shock to both of us. We would have understood if it had been chocolate cancer, but lung cancer seemed quite unlikely. We saw the PET CT-scan showing the cancer in her lungs and lymph nodes, and they lit up like a Christmas tree, *see* Figure 4. Immediately upon the diagnosis, an army of prayer warriors went to work. Our faith and trust in God kept us in relative peace. We both firmly believe that death, which was a distinct, almost very near term inevitability, is not the ultimate human tragedy. Death would mean the passing of the body, but a

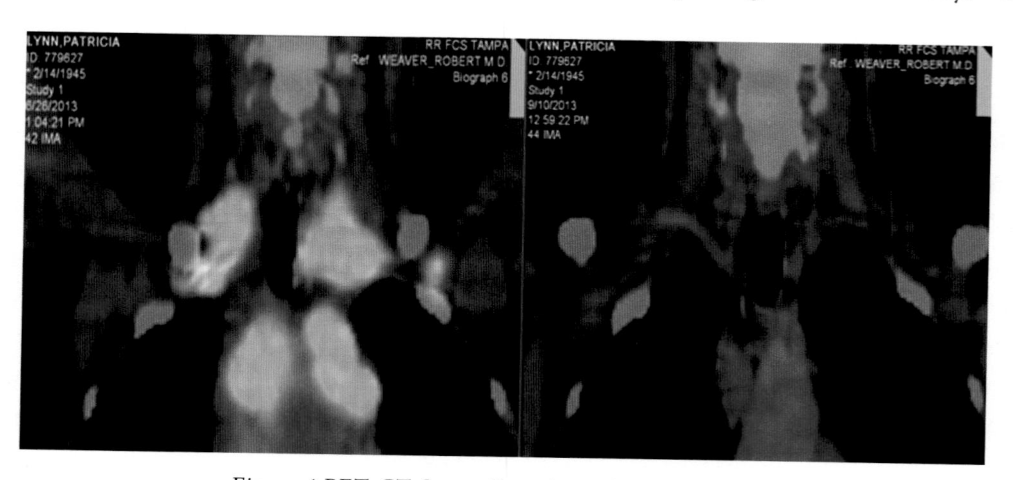

Figure 4 PET-CT-Scans, June 2013, September 2013

continuation of the eternal spirit created in her at her conception, and she would be united in Christ, seeing Him face to face. There would be a mighty pain of separation, but a trusting joy of her eternal happiness in the Beatific Vision.

There was also the firm and certain hope that we would be reunited in spirit when the day came that I, too, would cross over that bar. Our prayer was more to maintain our faith and trust than for healing. My wife felt an absolute buoyancy of prayers supporting her. Friends and family, tennis buddies, and a chain of people poured out an unrelenting torrent of prayer for her.

There were also innumerable corporal works of mercy showered upon both of us. My son is a doctor. Every report, every scan, every test result was sent to him. I cannot imagine the torture he went through, just as Our Blessed Mother endured at the foot of the Cross, seeing all these medical reports showing the slow, but certain, death of his mother. My daughter came to help out around the house and help her mother, later bringing her whole family for a joyous visit with us as we prepared for the cruise together. The whole family, down to the grandchildren, continued with plans for a cruise to the Bahamas, which we were able to enjoy, even though her condition was deteriorating. By the time of the cruise, a walk to the mailbox in our front yard and back into the house expended all her energy for the day. On the cruise, we used a collapsible wheel chair to maneuver her around the ship, and everyone joyfully took turns wheeling her around.

Upon our return from the cruise, our friends had organized themselves to bring us fresh, home cooked meals every few days; these meals were invariably everyone's favorite recipe. Although my wife ate and thoroughly enjoyed the meals her weight continued to decline. I, on the other hand, also enjoyed the meals and suffered no loss of weight. Throughout all of this, we both remained in good spirits, faithful, and full of trust in the goodness of God.

Just before we left on the cruise, we met with the doctor and got the final confirmation of the diagnosis: inoperable stage four lung cancer and there was no cure. However, there was one ray of hope. Among lifelong non-smokers, especially women, there was a possibility that my wife's cancer was caused by one of two genetic mutations, one designated ALK-mutation, the other EGFR-mutation. These are not inherited mutations. They are mutations that occur within the body, and these particular ones attack lung cells causing lung cancer. As we left for the cruise, my son, who is a radiologist and was in medical school with my wife's oncologist, received a text from our doctor that my wife had tested negative for the ALK-mutation, so they would begin testing for the second mutation.

While on the week-long cruise we were, for all intents and purposes, out of communication with the rest of the world. No email, no cell phones, no text messages, nothing by way of communication. It was a blessing that allowed us to enjoy the cruise without much thinking about the pending test results. We didn't worry much about it because we couldn't find out anyway. As we returned, even before the ship reached the pier, my son received a text message that my wife had tested positive for the EGFR-mutation. Now, the amazing work of God began to be revealed! We went to Patty's oncologist appointment to understand what this further diagnosis meant. Instead of debilitating bouts of chemotherapy and radiation, my wife's treatment would consist of a single pill that she would take once a day. Although the pill had been available for use during medical trials for several years, this pill had been approved as first line treatment of EGFR-mutation caused lung cancer in May of 2013, barely two months before we went on our cruise. It was as if the pill had been developed with her name on it. After taking the pill for two months a follow up PET CT-scan and doctor's appointment was scheduled to see if there had been any shrinkage of the tumors. We were both confident because she seemed to be improving dramatically. Her energy levels were higher, she began to take walks and deliberately exercise. There were a number of side effects, but compared to the alternative, they were miniscule—irritating and uncomfortable, but miniscule and certainly not like the effects of chemotherapy and radiation.

After the PET CT scan, we waited anxiously for the scheduled Friday appointment. Before that appointment, Patty received a call from her doctor. He said that he could not wait for two more days to give her the good news. The results were "much, much, much better than he expected!" He had told us going into the PET CT-scan that the proof of the effectiveness of the treatment would be shrinkage of the tumors. His reading of the PET CT-scan was that it showed the tumors were completely gone to the extent of being undetectable by the PET CT-scan and she was in remission. She had no detectable cancer tumors. From multiple three and four centimeter tumors, she had gone to no detectable tumors or cancer after two months of treatment. We all recognized that this was not a cure. There were still undetectable cancer cells in her body that could, once again, cause her symptoms to reoccur, but she was in remission.

A few years ago, stage-four lung cancer never went into remission. Even with modern treatment, complete remission is rare. So, we are faced with a devastating cancer diagnosis, an outpouring of prayer, tranquil, trusting faith, a specific treatment becoming available precisely when it was needed, and astounding results by all accounts. Clearly science, research, years of clinical trials, advanced diagnostic techniques, and well trained doctors are to be recognized and thanked. Certainly she is not the only person benefiting and receiving similar results from this treatment. And without a doubt, at some time she, like every other living thing, will die either of cancer or some other cause.

Was it miraculous? I think by any normal definition of miraculous wherein the laws of nature are set aside for a specific event and specific purpose, the answer would have to be, no, it was not miraculous. Ambrose Bierce offered a definition of prayer as follows:

> Pray. To ask the laws of the universe to be annulled on behalf of a single petitioner confessedly unworthy.[10]

On the other hand, secrets were revealed to researchers, doctors gained insight, timing was, for Patty, precisely exact, and the prayers have been copious and persistent. Further, the effect of prayer on our mental state, our faith, and our peace is undeniable. We have positively been lifted up and carried by prayer.

A few pages back, I considered the miraculous action of God to save the Israelites by parting the Red Sea so that they could cross to safety precisely at their moment of need. I said that I thought it would be no less a miracle for God to have arranged all the elements of the universe at the moment of Creation, the Big Bang, so that when the Israelites were confronted by the Red Sea in front and the hostile Egyptians behind, a mighty east wind began to blow through the night and parted the Red Sea for their safe passage. I am fully convinced that my wife's cancer treatment that brought her back from the brink of certain death with stage-four lung cancer to complete remission, not cured, but under control was an answer to prayer.

Consider all the things that fell into place with exquisite precision for this outcome. For years before her diagnosis, clinical studies, trials, and analyses were under way to detect and treat the very specific mutation from which she suffered. Both genetic mutations are rare, yet, she tested positive for one. The circumstances of her diagnosis were quite unusual. She had planned a minor surgery to be completed so that it would not interfere with the cruise being planned by my daughter for the whole family. After the surgery, everything appeared normal for a surgical recovery, except that she had no energy. The lack of energy was so severe that she consulted our family physician who ordered a chest X-ray. When he saw the X-ray, he said, "She has lung cancer."

A series of tests, procedures, biopsies, blood samples and the like were taken leading to the final diagnosis. Had she delayed the surgery until after the cruise, the X-ray may not have been taken. As a minimum her diagnosis would have been delayed, possibly fatally. If her cancer had appeared a few years ago, she might have been admitted to one of several drug trials to see how a particular drug might help her and, of course, her part of the trial may have been a placebo. A few more years before that, before these specific genetic mutations were identified and treatments were tailored to treat them, her treatment would have been conventional chemo-therapy and radiation, with near zero hope of remission. In all, too, too many things fell into place and came out exactly as she needed for the success of her treatment to have been anything but miraculous for someone looking "through the eyes of faith."

I began this discussion with the statement that I do not know how prayer works, but that I believe in it because the Bible, the words of the Lord, and the teaching of the Church attest to its value. I am content to accept and believe and give thanks to God for His Grace. Further, in all humility I recognize that God hides His truth from the eyes of the wise and reveals it to the child.

> **At that time Jesus said in reply, "I give praise to you, Father, Lord of heaven and earth, for although you have hidden these things from the wise and the learned you have revealed them to the childlike."**

Matthew 11:25.

So, I am obliged to simply accept the revealed truth that God hears our prayers and answers them in ways that are the very best for us and not necessarily exactly what we have prayed for. Indeed, Our Lord expounded on this very point to His disciples:

> **"And I tell you, ask and you will receive; seek and you will find; knock and the door will be opened to you. For everyone who asks, receives; and the one who seeks, finds; and to the one who knocks, the door will be opened. What father among you would hand his son a snake when he asks for a fish? Or hand him a scorpion when he asks for an egg? If you then, who are wicked, know how to give good gifts to your children, how much more will the Father in heaven give the holy Spirit to those who ask him?"**

Luke 11:10-13.

This, in fact, has been my experience in the writing of this book. As I have put pen to paper, or more precisely pecked at the keyboard of my computer, I have diligently reminded myself of the presence of the Lord. It has been my goal and my prayer that I write not my words, my thoughts, or my understanding, but that I write the words of the Lord, that I write only what He has inspired me to write.

Now, I must be very careful here. On one hand, I am not in any way implying that this collection of musings of my mind even approach the inspired Word of God revealed to us in Holy Scripture or the Holy Tradition held sacred by the Church in the preaching and writing of the Fathers of the Church. My effort crumbles into an insignificant pile of dust in comparison. However, I must also recognize and acknowledge the inspiration of the Holy Spirit as I conceived and wrote this book. I cannot count the number of times that I have become stuck or ensnared in my efforts to explain some point. Invariably, I have had to put it all aside and offer it to the Lord for His guidance. When I have prayed for the guidance of the Holy Spirit, placed myself in His Presence, and prayerfully contemplated the issue, without exception, although not in an instant or at a time of my choosing, a flash of clarification would come. I cannot present to you, my readers, any of these thoughts as anything more than my own ideas or thoughts I have learned from the writings of others, hopefully, thoroughly, and accurately attributed. At the same time, however, I truly do not believe these events were a product of my mind.

I am and always will be absolutely convinced that the Lord was giving me a direct answer to my prayer, and I was writing what He wanted me to write. To which all I can say is to repeat the motto of the Society of Jesus, the Jesuits, *Ad majorem Dei gloriam*—"To the greater glory of God."[11] And, should anything I have written in this book be in error, the fault is entirely my inability to properly convey the inspiration of the Holy Spirit.

Allow me to cite one specific, quite vivid example that happened within the last week as I am writing at this very moment. My son had taken his two children on a cruise around the Gulf of Mexico on vacation. They were accompanied on this vacation by another family, a strong Christian family, with two children, a boy and a girl, about the same ages as my grandchildren. My wife and I had the privilege of meeting them at the airport and, after a brief lunch, taking them to the cruise ship terminal. Upon their return, my wife and I again met them at the cruise ship terminal, this time more prudently in two cars, and returned them to the airport. Again, as it happened, I had in my car my son's friend's wife Nicole, her daughter, and my granddaughter, all piled in the back seat. As I drove the short trip to the airport, Nicole mentioned that my son had told her that I was writing a book, this book. I confessed that while that was true, I had not been very diligent lately, but I proceeded to give her a brief synopsis of the book while occasionally looking about at the morning traffic. We dropped them all off at the airport and said goodbye amid rounds of hugs and kisses, and that was that. Or, so I thought. That evening, I went to bed and quickly to sleep with no further thought about this book.

At this point, if I haven't digressed enough, let me digress again. In numerous instances the Bible describes people receiving a message from God in a dream. For example:

> **Joseph her husband, since he was a righteous man, yet unwilling to expose her to shame, decided to divorce her quietly. Such was his intention when, behold, the angel of the Lord appeared to him in a dream and said, "Joseph, son of David, do**

not be afraid to take Mary your wife into your home. For it is through the Holy Spirit that this child has been conceived in her. She will bear a son and you are to name him Jesus, because he will save his people from their sins."

Matthew 1:19-21.

I think that I have a much better and clearer understanding of what these dreams meant because of my experience, which I will now describe. As I said, I had had no further thoughts and offered no particular prayer about this book that evening. I simply went to sleep. It was a good, deep sleep, and I was not dreaming. But, I "heard," not with my ears, but inside my mind, myself ask the Lord, "What do you want me to do?"

I "heard," again, not with my ears, His response which was simple, direct, and utterly clear: "I already told you."

I knew instantly, without a moment's reflection, exactly what He meant. Nicole's question about my book had been a thoroughly missed message from Him to get busy. Get back to writing this book. Surprisingly, in retrospect, I slept through the night, but when I woke in the morning, this "dream" was vividly clear. I knew exactly what it meant and exactly what I needed to do. Let me add that normally when I have a dream, in the morning when I wake up, I may recall having had the dream but the details are usually incoherent. When I dream, I see images or pictures and hear sounds, though obviously neither through my normal senses. This was completely different. It was of a piece with all the other clarifications I believe I have received from the Lord. The exception was that I had made no request.

As I said, this event was very clear and very vivid to me, and I have absolutely no doubt that it was a specific message to me from the Lord. It was more effective than an appropriately placed size 10 boot. To you my readers, I can ask you to believe nothing more than, if you are reading this, I indeed got back to work.

Shortly after this event, my wife and I drove to Fort Leavenworth, Kansas to visit my daughter and her family. During the trip of 21 hours which we drove straight through, we listened to an audio book by Dr. Eben Alexander entitled *Proof of Heaven*. In his book, he describes a near death experience that profoundly changed his life. As we listened to the book he described the communication between his spiritual self, separated from his body and other spiritual beings during his encounter. I was so stunned by his description that I stopped the playback of the book and told my wife, "This is exactly what it was like for me when God communicated to me." This is what Dr. Alexander described:

> Although I still had little language function, at least as we think of it on Earth, I began wordlessly putting questions to this wind-and to the divine

> being that I sensed at work behind or within it.
>
> *Where is this place?*
>
> *Who am I?*
>
> *Why am I here?*
>
> Each time I silently posed one of these questions, the answer came instantly in an explosion of light, color, love, and beauty that blew through me like a crashing wave. What was important about these bursts was that they didn't simply silence my questions by overwhelming them. They *answered* them, but in a way that bypassed language. Thoughts entered me directly. But it wasn't thought like we experience on earth. It wasn't vague, immaterial, or abstract. These thoughts were solid and immediate-hotter than fire and wetter than water-and as I received them I was able to instantly and effortlessly understand concepts that would have taken me years to fully grasp in my earthly life. [12]

My personal communication did not include the "explosion of light, color, love, and beauty that blew through me like a crashing wave" that Doctor Alexander described, nor was my experience a near death experience as his was. But the communication process was identical. Questions were asked and answered without words. The answers were immediately understood without hesitation or effort. "*Hearing*" the voice of God was an immediate understanding. I have come to believe that we are indeed, meant to "hear" the voice of God. I am convinced that He will speak to us in ways we do not expect: through the Scriptures, in response to prayer, through the Holy Spirit speaking through our consciences, in dreams, through angels, and in myriad other ways. The Bible is explicit when it speaks to us:

> **Oh, that today you would hear his voice: Harden not your hearts.**

Hebrews 4:7.

Perhaps, God has spoken through another favorite medium—His Holy Word, the Bible. In our Bible Study Class at Church, two weeks ago, we studied the healing of a royal official's son in the fourth chapter St. John's Gospel pictured in Figure 5. The crucial issue is as follows:

> **The royal official said to him, "Sir, come down before my child dies." Jesus said to him, "You may go; your son will live." The man believed what Jesus said to him and left. While he was on his way back, his slaves met him and told him that his boy would live. He asked them when he began to recover. They told him, "The fever left him yesterday, about one in the afternoon." The father realized that just at that time Jesus had said to him, "Your son will live," and he and his whole household came to believe.**

John 4:46-54,

I think that the important understanding that this incident reveals is that God does not need us to tell Him our problems; He already knows. He does not need us to beg Him to help us in our need. He already will do whatever is best for us simply because He loves us. Prayer is not for God at all; it is for us. Consider the story of the royal official. When his son became deathly ill, he had two choices. He could pursue the usual remedies and ignore the healing power of Jesus a few miles away. Had he done so, his son would probably have died, and none of us would have ever heard his story. His second alternative would be to do exactly as he did, seek out Jesus, and pray for Jesus to save his son. Suppose that instead of waiting for the official to come to Him, Jesus, in His omniscience and omnipotence, had healed the lad just because he was in need. The problem would have been that no one would ever have known that he had been healed by the divine power of Jesus. No one would have come to faith in Him, which was by far the most important outcome of the story, because it affects the eternal life of the official and his whole household. Because of his prayer, he knew that it was the power of Jesus that saved his son and "he and his whole household came to believe," which had eternal ramifications.

We need to pray so we will know our own prayers have been answered and our faith will be strengthened. I now believe that our prayers and the prayers of so many faithful Christians have led directly to the healing of my wife. I know that sometime in the future, she will surely die, either of her lung cancer or through some other cause. But, she has been healed for now, and those prayers have strengthened the faith of more people than I can count. And, that is how I think prayer works; certainly not in completeness, but in an attempt by a rational mind and earnest faith to understand prayer.

Figure 5 Healing of the royal official's son

One World

One of the problems facing Christians when we consider creation, evolution, and scientific discoveries in general is language. We tend to use a different language in church than in everyday life.

I grew up in a Protestant faith experience, using primarily the King James Bible. Our Scripture, and therefore our prayers, were based on old English language. To this day, though now a Catholic, I easily lapse back into that language style. For example, when praying the Hail Mary, I will pray, "Hail Mary full of Grace, the Lord is with *thee.* Blessed *art thou* among women and blessed is the fruit of *thy* womb, Jesus."

Of course, the experience of my schoolmates who were Catholic was not much different, except they used Latin. While I was praying,

> Our Father, who art in heaven, hallowed be Thy name. Thy kingdom come. Thy will be done on earth as it is in heaven...

they were praying,

> Pater noster, qui es in caelis, sanctificetur nomen tuum. Adveniat regnum tuum. Fiat voluntas tua, sicut in caelo et in terra...

In both cases, the language of Church was significantly different from the language of our lives. In ordinary conversation or writing we no longer say "thee," "thou," or "art"—and certainly we were no speaking Latin. Today, this is a style of speech reserved for Church.

The result of this was, at least, a subconscious compartmentalization of the world of religion from the world we see around us, the world of our daily lives. This carries forward into our thinking about science and the discoveries being made about our world. I would hazard to guess that most people of faith, when asked about the Great Flood story of Noah in Genesis, would consider it to be just an interesting Bible story with a moral and religious message. Most people would not consider the real life, historical setting which such an event could be based upon.

For example, a scientific basis, such as the end of the Ice Age, when worldwide sea levels rose some 400 feet could very well have been the historical setting of the story of Noah, as well as hundreds of similar great flood stories around the world. I think this wonderful Bible story is in all likelihood a story passed down through countless generations until it was ultimately written down in what was to become Holy Scripture. A real life, historical basis for the story does nothing to reduce the moral and religious message contained in the Bible. The basis for the scientific consideration of the Great Flood will be addressed in later chapters. However, it is a nice illustration of the one world concept—that the world of Bible stories, the world we live in, and the world of scientific discoveries are all one world. "Through the eyes of faith," we can add richness to our faith without compromising logical scientific reasoning. In so doing, both the science and our faith become easier, not harder, to believe.

Another implication of the one world concept is that if the science is rigorously tested and verified (sadly that is not always the case) then we can, with some caveats accept it as truth. Likewise, if our faith is based on sound principles revealed to us by God, disseminated by faithful disciples, attested to by the blood of martyrs, and handed down to us by the Church guided by the Holy Spirit, that too, may be accepted as truth. But if both are true, yet in appearance at times somewhat contradictory, we must combine our faith and our reason, both gifts of God, to reconcile the differences. That is the endeavor upon which this book embarks.

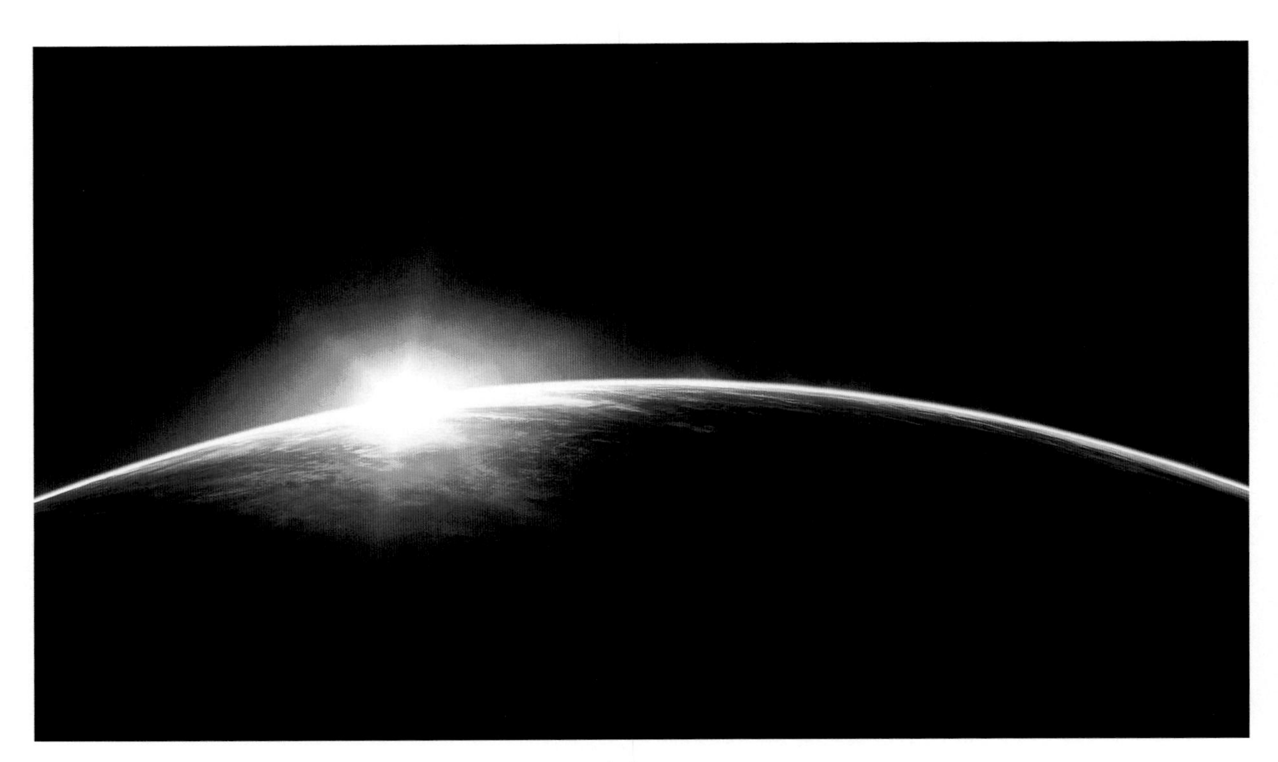

Figure 6 Earth from space sunrise

SCIENTIFIC THEORY AND MODELS

I Believe / I Think

One of the ways we can help ourselves sort through the dilemma of faith and science is to be precise in our language. Faith is a gift from God that enables us to accept revelation from the Holy Spirit. It requires both Grace from God and a positive response from the individual. The *Catechism of the Catholic Church* explains this action and response duality much better than I can:

> *Faith is a grace*
>
> 153 When St. Peter confessed that Jesus is the Christ, the Son of the living God, Jesus declared to him that this revelation did not come "from flesh and blood", but from "my Father who is in heaven." Faith is a gift of God, a supernatural virtue infused by him. "Before this faith can be exercised, man must have the grace of God to move and assist him; he must have the interior helps of the Holy Spirit, who moves the heart and converts it to God, who opens the eyes of the mind and 'makes it easy for all to accept and believe the truth.'"[13]
>
> *Faith is a human act*
>
> 154 Believing is possible only by grace and the interior helps of the Holy Spirit. But it is no less true that believing is an authentically human act. Trusting in God and cleaving to the truths he has revealed is contrary neither to human freedom nor to human reason. Even in human relations it is not contrary to our dignity to believe what other persons tell us about themselves and their intentions, or to trust their promises (for example, when a

> man and a woman marry) to share a communion of life with one another. If this is so, still less is it contrary to our dignity to "yield by faith the full submission...of intellect and will to God who reveals," and to share in an interior communion with him.[14]

Science, on the other hand, is a rigorous process of observation, development of a model or hypothesis that predicts future results, and testing the model or hypothesis against further observations.

In this book, I will use the convention of "I believe" to indicate something which I accept as a matter of faith through divine revelation taught by the Catholic Church. Whereas, those things I can determine by my own senses, reason, or logic, or which have been rigorously tested through the scientific method, I refer to using the convention, "I think" or "I accept." Allow me to offer some examples, which will be further developed in later chapters.

⇒*I believe* that God created the universe and everything in it out of nothing. He created it by His Word, and without His creative action, nothing exists.

⇒*I think* that the process of creation can be reasonably described by the Big Bang Theory without contradicting the Biblical account. At the instant of the Big Bang, all matter and energy in the universe and the existence of time itself instantly appeared without reference to pre-existing matter.

⇒*I believe* that the initial spark of life was not a random chemical event or a crystal from space. It was a unique act of God originating life where there was none before.

⇒*I think* that every living thing evolved from the first living entity that sprang into being from inorganic material, i.e. clay.

⇒*I think* that the process of creation of all living things may be reasonably explained by an evolutionary model and that the human species is the product of such a model. Evolution is a scientific model describing the process God used in the development of all living things, including man,

⇒*I believe* that God created Adam and Eve, parents of all humanity; from the natural elements of his Creation, specifically clay, and that he infused in them a spiritual element unique from every other animal in creation, and that this spiritual element is the image of God Himself.

⇒*I think* that Adam and Eve were real people who lived approximately 150,000 years ago in Africa from whom every living human being descended.

⇒*I think* that the God infused spirit makes human beings, Homo Spiritus, unique from every other animal, including other hominid species.

⇒*I believe* that the infusion of the spirit was not an evolutionary event, rather it was specific act of God repeated at the conception of every human being.

⇒*I think* that scientific studies of human DNA provide a persuasive argument that all human beings currently living are the descendants of a single male and single female ancestor.

⇒*I believe* that Noah was a real living person inspired by God to build an Ark that would provide for the safety of himself, his family, his domesticated animals, and wild animals from a cataclysmic worldwide flood.

⇒*I think* that during a warming period after an Ice Age, continental glaciers melted rapidly causing a rise in sea level on the order of 400 feet worldwide. While this rise in sea level was gradual over decades, in instances where natural barriers were ultimately breached, water flooded catastrophically into low lying areas destroying all human and animal inhabitants. I deduce from this that survival from this type of sudden inundation would be achieved by having a previously prepared boat, or Ark, just as Noah is described as building in the Bible.

Scientific Theory

In order to address the relationship between scientific theory and faith, it is necessary to specify in precise terms exactly what a scientific theory is. For that definition, I defer to the Nobel laureate, Stephen Hawking. In his book, *The Illustrated A Brief History of Time*, he defines a scientific theory:

> A theory is just a model of the universe, or a restricted part of it, and a set of rules that relate quantities in the model to observations we make. It exists only in our minds and does not have any other reality (whatever that might mean.) A theory is a good theory if it satisfies two requirements. It must accurately describe a large class of observations on the basis of a model that contains only a few arbitrary elements, and it must make definite predictions about the results of future observations.

He goes on to say:

> A theory is always provisional, in the sense that it is always a hypothesis: you can never prove it. No matter how many times the results of experiments agree with some theory, you can never be sure that the next time the result will not contradict the theory. On the other hand, you can disprove the theory by finding even a single observation that disagrees with the predictions of the theory. A philosopher of science, Karl Poppe,r has emphasized, a good theory is characterized by the fact that it makes a number of predictions that could, in principle, be disproved or falsified by observation. Each time new experiments are observed to agree with the predictions, the theory survives, and our

confidence in it is increased; but if ever a new observation is found to disagree, we have to abandon or modify the theory."[15]

One observation that can immediately be made about a scientific theory is that it is never "settled science" or a "scientific consensus." Indeed, those phrases are oxymoronic. If it is science, it is neither settled nor a consensus. If there is a consensus or it is settled, it is no longer science. By way of illustration of this fact and the general definition of a scientific theory, it is useful to consider the scientific theory concerning the propagation of light.

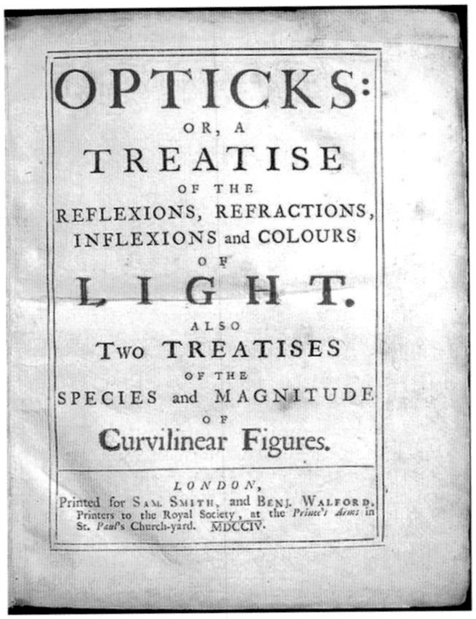

OPTICKS:
OR, A
TREATISE
OF THE
REFLEXIONS, REFRACTIONS, INFLEXIONS and COLOURS
OF
LIGHT.
ALSO
Two TREATISES
OF THE
SPECIES and MAGNITUDE
OF
Curvilinear Figures.

LONDON,
Printed for SAM. SMITH, and BENJ. WALFORD, Printers to the Royal Society, at the Prince's Arms in St. Paul's Church-yard. MDCCIV.

Figure 7 Optiks by Sir Isaac Newton, 1704

In 1704, in a treatise describing the propagation of light entitled *Optiks*, Sir Isaac Newton proposed the theory that light traveled through a medium called luminiferous aether or ether. Briefly, his description was as follows:

> Is not the Heat of the warm Room convey'd through the vacuum by the Vibrations of a much subtiler Medium than Air, which after the Air was drawn out remained in the Vacuum? And is not this Medium the same with that Medium by which Light is refracted and reflected, and by whose Vibrations Light communicates Heat to Bodies, and is put into Fits of easy Reflexion and easy Transmission?[16]

In 1905, Albert Einstein presented a paper called, "On the Electrodynamics of Moving Bodies," that proposed the Special Theory of Relativity. This theory described the propagation of light without resorting to luminiferous aether and, in effect, corrected Newtonian mechanics to handle situations where objects are moving at close to the speed of light. Newton, Einstein had discovered, was wrong.

Sir Isaac Newton's theory on the propagation of light was "settled science" for over two hundred years. Yet today, it is considered to be a superseded theory.

Under the definitions of Stephen Hawking and Karl Popper, a theory must be discarded or modified when its predictions are at variance with observation. However, it is possible for a superseded theory, such as Newton's now discredited theory of luminiferous aether, to provide useful descriptions of the universe without being one hundred percent correct in all observations or, as Einstein observed, in all conditions. Again, we turn to the nature of light as an example.

There are two models for the propagation of light, the particle model and the wave model. Neither is a complete description, but both are useful analytical tools.

In the particle model, light behaves like a particle with no mass, called a photon. It will bounce off a reflecting surface in the same manner as a particle; think of a rubber ball bouncing off a wall. An interesting scientific device known as a radiometer provides a simple demonstration of this particle model of light. When light photons impact the paddles, delicately balanced in an evacuated bulb, the paddles will begin to rotate as if they had been struck by tiny, invisible rubber balls.

Figure 8 Radiometer

In the wave model, light behaves like a wave with a frequency and a wavelength. These two characteristics form a proportional relationship with the speed of light, which is always a constant. As the wavelength changes, so too, will the frequency in a proportional manner. The most obvious characteristic of changing wavelength is the color of the light. As light passes through a medium and is caused to bend, the different wavelengths will bend by differing amounts producing a spectrum or rainbow of colors.

Indeed, this is exactly what causes the rainbow we see as the Sun shines through the falling rain. In the laboratory, we see the same effect by passing light through a prism.

So, one may ask, "Which is it? Is light a particle or a wave?" The answer is both. Both are useful models for describing different properties of light.

As we address some of the modern scientific theories and models relating to creation and the rise of mankind, it is important to recognize that all of the scientific discussions are theories precisely as Stephen Hawking has defined them. "It exists only in our minds and does not have any other reality." [15]

They are useful in understanding the nature of our universe and the processes we see unfolding. We will address these theories in later chapters looking at them "through the eyes of faith."

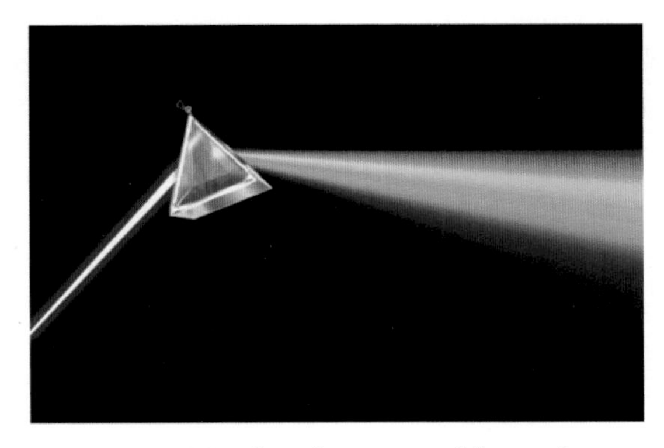

Figure 9 Wavelengths separated by a prism

I would like to make observations about the Big Bang, which, as stated, I consider to be a sound scientific model describing the event of Creation. A lot of misunderstanding surrounds the term Big Bang. Although, it would certainly be considered "settled science" these days, there are a number of flaws that do not withstand scrutiny. I should point out the unfortunate term, "Big Bang," was given to the theory as a term of approbation by one who was unconvinced. Fred Hoyle, described in his 2001 obituary as a "cosmologist and controversialist," coined the term in a moment of facetiousness, for a radio broadcast in 1952.[17]

Figure 10 The "Big Bang," as commonly viewed

Consider this:

- It was not big, in the sense of size. Indeed, it was infinitesimally small. All of the matter and energy of the universe was condensed into a point of zero size and infinite density.
- It was not a bang. In fact, there was no sound at all. Sound requires matter to propagate. At the instant of Creation, however, there was nothing outside the infinitely small singularity. Therefore, there was no sound. From this we get the answer to the old conundrum, "If a tree falls in the forest and there is no one around to hear it, did it make a sound?" If there is no matter through which to propagate, there is no sound.
- There was no flash of light. As we shall see shortly, the energy was so high at the instant of Creation, that there was no energy in the visible light spectrum as visualized in Figure 8. Indeed, it would be 300,000 years before the universe had expanded enough and cooled enough for energy to fall within the visible light spectrum...

at which point, God said, "Let there be light."

TIME

Having established the starting point for temporal time, it is also necessary to consider the vast distinction between the orderly sequence of events that we call time and the completely overarching concept of eternity outside of time in God's eyes. This concept is so extraordinary beyond human comprehension that the best I can do is present something of an analogy that I think is consistent with Church teaching. The Catechism of the Catholic Church teaches the following:

> 600 To God, all moments of time are present in their immediacy.[18]

This teaching is completely consistent with the essential characteristics of God, His omnipotence, omnipresence, and His omniscience. Each of these characteristics requires study, prayer and contemplation to comprehend. But, even then our understanding is incomplete. I think the last of these characteristics, omniscience, is the most difficult to understand, especially, as it pertains to time because, as human beings we live in a time ordered domain. Indeed, in our modern world, time becomes an obsession. We awaken to an alarm clock. We scurry to successive appointments, each with its specified time. We are lost without a watch. But, everything is sequential and time ordered. We cannot go back in time, except in our memories, and we cannot go beyond the present, except by speculation and guess work. It may be well founded analysis that forms our predictions of future events, but it is still a guess, never a certainty.

God, on the other hand, is Spirit, and as such exists outside of time. There is no before or after, no past or future; there is only now. And, that now covers the full expanse of time and more. Dr. Schroeder adds that even the name of God, given to Moses from the burning bush in Exodus contains this concept:

> The concept of the Eternal Now is implied in the explicit four letter name of God (Exodus 3:14). In the Hebrew, the spelling includes the letters of the verb "to be" in its three tenses: I was, I am, I will be. The past, present, and future are all contained within the Eternal.[19]

Modern science posits the beginning of the universe, Creation, at the Big Bang approximately 14.7 billion years ago. That event set into motion the "clocks" of the universe. St. Augustine describes the instant of Creation by God as the beginning of time in his book, *The City of God*, written about AD 413.

> That the creation of the world and the beginning of time both occurred simultaneously, and that the one did not come before the other.[20]

Since time began at that moment, there is no possibility of examining events that occurred "before" the Big Bang. Nothing can be measured; nothing can be tested or verified in any way before the Big Bang. In science, to do so is pure speculation and guesswork without any scientific basis; it is simply not science. The Nobel Laureate Stephen Hawking states:

> If there were events earlier than this time, then they could not affect what happens at the present time. Their existence can be ignored because it would have no observational consequences.[21]

In matters of faith we are free, indeed, required to look at matters far beyond the realm of provable science into the realm of divine revelation. As a matter of faith, we believe that the creation of the universe was preceded by the existence of God. It was at His Word that the universe came into existence. We believe that there has never been a time when God has not existed and there will never be a time when God will not exist. We believe that God was, is, and always will be. Yet, in these very sentences the problem is revealed. As human beings we simply cannot think outside of time. Words such as "before", "preceded", "came", "was", "will be" are all time oriented, but God exists outside of time. This is a difficult concept because, as human beings, we exist in a time ordered universe, so we have to stretch our minds to conceive of existence outside of time. But a timeless existence is not just a theological concept; it is a scientific reality experimentally proved by Albert Einstein. As one scholar explained,

> Einstein theorized, and later experiments proved, that the faster on travels relative to another object, the slower time flows for the traveler relative to the flow of time measured by the stationary observer. At the speed of light (the highest speed attainable in our universe), time ceases to flow altogether. The time of all events becomes compressed into the present, an

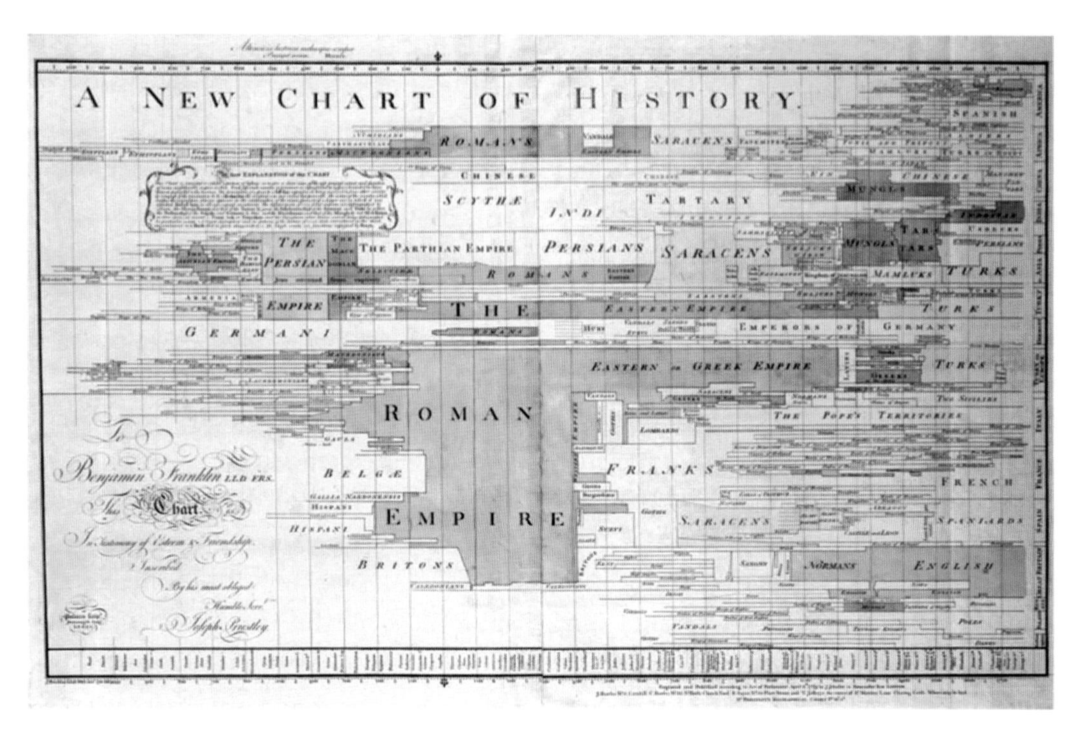

Figure 11 *Historical timeline*

unending now.[22]

One way to look at God existing outside of time is to consider a historical timeline, such as the one illustrated in Figure 11, prepared by Joseph Priestly, 1733-1804. I recognize that this timeline is difficult to read, but viewing the history of the world at a glance may require one to squint.

With this timeline before Him, imagine God looking at every point in the timeline, extending back before the beginning of this timeline to the moment of Creation, 14.7 billion years ago, and forward to the Last Day and the General Resurrection. Further, God's timeline stretches for all eternity, before creation of the Heavens and the Earth and beyond the Last Day, (although these temporal references, "before" and "beyond" are meaningless in eternity.) The description of Creation in St. John's Gospel clearly portrays Jesus, the Divine Word, as the instrument of Creation pre-existing the Creation event:

> **In the beginning was the Word, and the Word was with God, and the Word was God. He was in the beginning with God. All things came to be through him, and without him nothing came to be.**

John 1:1-3.

Note that the illustrated timeline depicts the empires of the world. Of course, God's timeline would depict not only empires, but would include every event of the life of every human being who ever lived or who ever would live. For each person it would begin at the moment God created each person's immortal soul and inserted it into the unborn baby at the very instant of conception. It would extend through every moment of life, death, judgment, resurrection on the Last Day, and would extend infinitely throughout eternity. In this description, the validity of time can be accepted for the moment of conception to death, but time becomes irrelevant at the moment of death because that person has entered into eternity.

But even this does not capture the extent of God's timeline (nor, of course can we ever hope to). Nevertheless, as we look closer at God's timeline we see that God knows every event of our lives, He also knows our innermost thoughts.

> **Behold, I know your thoughts, and the arguments you rehearse against me.**

Job 21:27.

> **The Lord knows the thoughts of the wise, that they are vain.**

1 Corinthians 3:20.

Yet, even this does not capture the depth of God's timeline, because not only does He know every human being to the depths of their thoughts, He also knows every beast of the field and bird in the air. They are all a part of His creation; He loves them and He knows them.

> **Are not two sparrows sold for a small coin? Yet not one of them falls to the ground without your Father's knowledge.**

Matthew 10:29.

You capture a small inkling of the irrelevance of time and see the basis for the Catechism reference,

> 600 To God, all moments of time are present in their immediacy.[23]

in Jesus' discussion with the Jewish religious authorities about Abraham in the eighth chapter of St. John's Gospel:

> **Abraham your father rejoiced to see my day; he saw it and was glad. So the Jews said to him, "You are not yet fifty years old and you have seen Abraham?" Jesus said to them, "Amen, amen, I say to you, before Abraham came to be, I AM."**

John 8:56-58.

Notice that just because God has His timeline and knows our every thought and action, He in no way inhibits our free will or our choices. He has given us His Word in Holy Scripture, in the Holy Spirit guided teachings of the Church, and the ever present Incarnation of His Word in Jesus Christ, Our Lord. With these we have every piece of information and every holy inspiration we need to live a Christ centered life. That God already knows the choices we will make does not diminish our personal responsibility for them.

> 600 When therefore he establishes his eternal plan of "predestination", he includes in it each person's free response to his grace.[24]

Finally, in the book of Revelation, Our Lord announces His existence in timeless eternity at least three times:

> **"I am the Alpha and the Omega," says the Lord God, "the one who is and who was and who is to come, the almighty."**

Revelation 1:8.

I think that this description of the timelessness of God has significant ramifications for our concept of prayer. Our prayers are not necessary for God to know our innermost needs, desires, and issues. He knows them far more than we ourselves know them. Prayer is important so that we live our lives in the Presence of the Lord. He is already present in the life of every human being at every moment of our existence. But, we need to have that recognition. We need to recognize that God's loving presence completely surrounds us at every moment. We need to place ourselves in His presence. If we recognize that we are in the presence of God, we would, or at least should, live our lives very differently. Figure 12 is an attempt by 16th Century artist, Correggio to capture "a glimpse into God's infinite dimensions."[25] The attempt is noble and raises the mind to ponder God in His fullness, but as all such mortal exercises it must fall short. Even the term "infinite dimensions" is an oxymoron.

Another implication to our understanding of prayer is that it does not matter when we pray. As Catholics, we believe in the communion of saints. We believe that praying for one another is beneficial for ourselves and for those for whom we pray. Some may doubt there is value praying for people after they have died. They have made all the choices of their lives and nothing will change that after death.

Figure 12 Correggio's "Assumption of the Virgin"
"A glimpse into God's infinite dimensions"

However, if prayer for another is

beneficial while that person lives, then prayer at any other time would have precisely the same benefits, because God knew long before our prayer was ever uttered what that prayer would be and what grace it would ask for, and He would act upon it in His gracious way. Prayer for our ancestors is every bit as effective as prayer for our descendants because, "[t]o God, all moments of time are present in their immediacy."

Senses of Scripture

Before embarking upon the investigation of scientific discoveries "through the eyes of faith," we need to review some of the Church's teachings that will guide our application of faith to scientific discoveries. The first of these is the Church's instruction on how we should study the Bible.

When we read the Bible, the Church teaches us be attentive to both the literal sense of the events, the people, and the actions that are described in the passage. We are also to be attentive to the spiritual sense which the passage is conveying.

The Catechism defines the senses of scripture as follows:

> The Senses of Scripture
>
> 115 According to an ancient tradition, one can distinguish between two senses of Scripture: the literal and the spiritual, the latter being subdivided into the allegorical, moral and anagogical senses. the profound concordance of the four senses guarantees all its richness to the living reading of Scripture in the Church.[26]
>
> 116 The literal sense is the meaning conveyed by the words of Scripture and discovered by exegesis, following the rules of sound interpretation: "All other senses of Sacred Scripture are based on the literal."[27]
>
> 117 The spiritual sense. Thanks to the unity of God's plan, not only the text of Scripture but also the realities and events about which it speaks can be signs.
>
> 1. The allegorical sense. We can acquire a more profound understanding of events by recognizing their significance in Christ; thus the crossing of the Red Sea is a sign or type of Christ's victory and also of Christian Baptism.
>
> 2. The moral sense. the events reported in Scripture ought to lead us to act justly. As St. Paul says, they were written "for our instruction."
>
> 3. The anagogical sense (Greek: anagoge, "leading"). We can view realities and events in terms of their eternal significance, leading us toward our true homeland: thus the Church on earth is a

sign of the heavenly Jerusalem.[28]

Although the Bible is filled with examples of the spiritual sense, indeed that is its primary purpose, a few simple examples are in order to further illuminate the Church's teaching. For example, in the twenty-second chapter of Genesis we read the story God commanding Abraham to take his son up on the mountain and sacrifice him to God. Of course, God never intends the sacrifice to be completed and stops Abraham before he completes the act. In the literal sense, we can see God testing Abraham's faith to prove the completeness of his faith. Keep in mind that God did not need the proof. He already knew Abraham's heart. The real proof was to Abraham, that he would know that the completeness of his faith and that his faith was well placed; God would never allow him to do such a thing. It is the spiritual sense, in particular the analogical sense, that is so striking. On the way up the mountain, the following exchange takes place between Abraham and Isaac:

> **As the two walked on together, Isaac spoke to his father Abraham. "Father!" he said. "Yes, son," he replied. Isaac continued, "Here are the fire and the wood, but where is the sheep for the holocaust?" "Son," Abraham answered, "God himself will provide the sheep for the holocaust."**

Genesis 22:7-8.

In the literal sense, Abraham is talking about the sheep that he will ultimately find caught in the thicket after the angel of God stops the killing of Isaac. But in the analogical sense, the lamb provided by God is none other than Jesus Christ, the beloved Son of God, who will obediently endure the completion of the sacrifice by His Passion and death on the cross. It is He that John the Baptist refers to as the Lamb of God, firmly connecting Our Lord to the sacrificial sheep offered in place of Isaac, the father of God's Chosen People, and to the Passover lambs sacrificed to save the Chosen People from death in the final plague against Egypt as God led them out of bondage in Egypt.

The Old Testament and New Testament are literally filled with examples of the moral sense of Scripture—teaching us how to live in harmony with our God and with our fellow man. It is instructive to see how teaching develops through the Bible. Using another example from Genesis, God gives Abram a very simple, yet complete instruction on how to live:

> **When Abram was ninety-nine years old, the LORD appeared to him and said: "I am God the Almighty. Walk in my presence and be blameless."**

Genesis 17:1.

That's it. Simply put, God is saying if you wouldn't do it in front of your mother, don't do it; or more directly, don't do anything you would not do in front of Me, your eternal judge, because whether you believe it or not, you are doing it in front of Me.. Later, in the Book of Exodus, God gives Moses the Ten Commandments. Although not as concise as the commandment given to Abram, the Ten Commandments are still clear and represent a good guide to living in harmony with God and our fellow man. As time goes by, additional rules and regulations are added in the Old Testament. In addition, commentaries were written to more fully explain the Ten Commandments and the additional regulations. For example, the Command to keep the Sabbath is given in Exodus:

> **Remember to keep holy the Sabbath day. Six days you may labor and do all your work, but the seventh day is the Sabbath of the LORD, your God. No work may be done then either by you, or your son or daughter, or your male or female slave, or your beast, or by the alien who lives with you. In six days the LORD made the heavens and the earth, the sea and all that is in them; but on the seventh day he rested. That is why the LORD has blessed the Sabbath day and made it holy.**

Exodus 20:8-11.

That still left open the question of what constituted work that was forbidden on the Sabbath. So, additional rules were formulated defining work. In our Lord's time, Jesus, as well as some other contemporary rabbis, once again simplified Our God's instructions on how to live in the following exchange:

> **"Teacher, which commandment in the law is the greatest?" He said to him, "You shall love the Lord, your God, with all your heart, with all your soul, and with all your mind. This is the greatest and the first commandment. The second is like it: You shall love your neighbor as yourself. The whole law and the prophets depend on these two commandments."**

Matthew 22:36-40.

Finally, Our Lord further simplified our moral instructions by directing that His followers compare their actions with the example they had seen in His life:

> **This is my commandment: love one another as I love you. No one has greater love than this, to lay down one's life for one's friends.**

John 15:12-13.

I say He simplified the law, which He does, but He invokes an unattainable standard. Nevertheless, that is the standard, the goal of our lives, to live and love as He did. He has brought us full circle; right back to the rule God gave Abram. It is the rule many people wear on rubber bracelets: "WWJD—What Would Jesus Do?" Or simply, live your lives in the presence of our Lord and act as He would act. This the moral sense of Scripture.

The third of the spiritual senses is the "anagogical sense." This is the sense that is concerned with how a particular passage of scripture addresses our eternal future.

While there are many examples of the "anagogical sense" in individual passages of the Old Testament, a relatively clear example is to simply look at the salvation history of the Chosen People from Abraham up to the entry into the Promised Land. The Lord made a promise to Abraham to give him the land which He, the Lord God, had led him to on the basis of Abraham's faith from the land of Ur.

> **The LORD appeared to Abram and said, "To your descendants I will give this land."**

Genesis 12:7.

In the literal sense, this was the Promised Land. It was a land the Lord would describe in detail with specific, discernible landmarks. It was a land which Abraham would never see in his lifetime as his possession, yet he retained his faith that his descendants would receive it.

Although there is a fair amount of controversy over the time period of Abraham, it has been dated to approximately 2300 BC. The nineteenth century book, *Early History of the Hebrews* reasoned,

> Professor Sayce, from the connexion of Abraham with Amraphel in the episode related in Genesis, xiv, says that "we can approximately fix the period when the family of Terah migrated from Ur of the Chaldees. It was about 2300 B.C., if the chronology of the native Babylonian historians is correct."[29]

However, the Hebrews did not enter into the Promised Land until Joshua led them across the Jordan, after the release from captivity in Egypt and the wandering in the wilderness. It was 41 years after the beginning of the Exodus or about 1236 BC. As one scholar observed,

> The Book of Josue [Joshua] contains two parts: the conquest of the Promised Land and the division thereof. (a) The Conquest (i- xii). Josue [Joshua] enters the land of promise, after being assured by spies that the way is safe. It is the tenth day of the first month, forty-one years since the Exodus.[30]

Therefore, it was more than a thousand years from the time of God's promise to Abraham until the Hebrews finally entered the Promised Land to possess. Yet even this date is only the date of entry. It will not be until the time Solomon—sometime between 967 BC and 927 BC—that the full extent of the Promised Land will be something Israel can call their land. By the year 586 BC, all of the Promised Land had fallen to invaders, Jerusalem and the Temple destroyed, and the Israelites carried into captivity. Although the people would return to Jerusalem and rebuild the Temple, they would always be under foreign domination. What then to make of God's promise of a land to the descendants of

Abraham if it were only to be for a brief period of ownership.

The answer to that question is found in the "anagogical sense" of the Scriptures. The land possessed by Joshua and those that followed him were merely a prototype of the eternal Promised Land. This eternal Promised Land, or heaven is the "land" that would possessed by the descendants of Abraham, not descendants of the flesh, but descendants in the faith. St. Paul eloquently describes descendants in the flesh in his letter to the Romans.

> **It was not through the law that the promise was made to Abraham and his descendants that he would inherit the world, but through the righteousness that comes from faith. For this reason, it depends on faith, so that it may be a gift, and the promise may be guaranteed to all his descendants, not to those who only adhere to the law but to those who follow the faith of Abraham, who is the father of all of us.**

Romans 4:13, 16.

The Letter to the Hebrews is more specific in differentiating the Promised Land entered by Joshua with the Israelites from the eternal Promised Land that all faithful Christians will enter after their death –called God's rest in Hebrews. There are many Southern Gospel hymns that describe death, judgment, and entry into heaven as crossing the Jordan.

> **Now if Joshua had given them rest, he would not have spoken afterwards of another day. Therefore, a Sabbath rest still remains for the people of God. And whoever enters into God's rest, rests from his own works as God did from his. Therefore, let us strive to enter into that rest, so that no one may fall after the same example of disobedience.**

Hebrews 4:8-11.

So let us look back over the history of the Chosen People from their captivity in Egypt to their crossing the Jordan River into the Promised Land in the "anagogical sense" of Scripture:

- God sent Moses, an analogical figure of Christ, to save His Chosen People from slavery in Egypt.
- After nine plagues called down upon Egypt and their false gods, God sent the angel of death to strike the first born of all of Egypt, man and beast, except for those of His Chosen People who had marked their homes with the blood of the Passover Lamb. Again this is an analogical figure of Christ, the Lamb of God who saved His people, all of mankind, by shedding His blood. But, the salvation of His faithful people by Christ was an anagogical event because the faithful are led by Christ to eternal life with Him.
- Moses, the analogical Christ, leads

His people through the Red Sea, saving them from the evil intended for them by Pharaoh's pursuing army. This event is an analogue of our baptism in which we are immersed in water, symbolizing dying with Christ, and then rising from the water with our past sins expunged, symbolizing the Resurrection of Christ and our resurrection with Him at the end of our lives.

- Moses received the Law from God on Mt. Sinai and delivered the Law to the Israelites as a guide for living in harmony with God and with their fellow men.

The Catechism teaches,

> 1961 God, our Creator and Redeemer, chose Israel for himself to be his people and revealed his Law to them, thus preparing for the coming of Christ. The Law of Moses expresses many truths naturally accessible to reason. These are stated and authenticated within the covenant of salvation.[31]

During His earthly ministry Christ taught and preached to make the precepts of the Law understandable. Notably, the Sermon on the Mount is an expression of God's Law. However, the greatest expression of God's Law was His life. Through His perfect obedience even unto death on the cross, Our Lord demonstrated the true and authentic expression of God's Law. So perfect was His example that He could tell his disciples in a single sentence the entire meaning of the Law:

> **This is my commandment: love one another as I love you.**

John 15:12.

The forty years wandering in the wilderness led by Moses with the column of smoke by day and the column of fire by night is an analogue of the Church Militant, Christians today, are wandering through a hostile world. We are led by Christ, present as the Body of Christ, His Holy Church, and guided by the Holy Spirit as we journey toward the Promised Land. Like the Children of Israel, we often fail in our faith and turn away from God in the disobedience of sin. Through the Sacrament of Reconciliation, we are forgiven as God repeatedly forgave the Israelites. We are also like the Israelites who were fed by manna, the bread come down from heaven, and the water that flowed from the side of the rock. But, we are sustained by the true Bread come down from heaven, the very Body, Blood, soul, and divinity of Christ in the Eucharist. We also receive the Living Water that flowed from the wound in Our Lord's side as He hung on the cross; only with this water, we never thirst again. Finally, after forty years wandering in the wilderness, the Israelites crossed the Jordan River and entered the Promised Land.

Like the Israelites of the Bible, each individual comes to the end of life and crosses the anagogical river Jordan—our body gives up our spirit, the very image of God breathed into us by God at our conception. That spirit containing our mind, our will, our memory, our personality, indeed everything that makes us a unique individual, comes before God in judgment. At that point, our eternal destiny is determined, once and forever, either to eternal bliss with our God in heaven for those who have remained faithful to the end, or into the anguish of eternal separation from God, condemned not by God, but by our own willful and final rejection of God in the course of our lives. This eternal separation, the Church calls Hell.

> 1033 We cannot be united with God unless we freely choose to love him. But we cannot love God if we sin gravely against him, against our neighbor or against ourselves: "He who does not love remains in death. Anyone who hates his brother is a murderer, and you know that no murderer has eternal life abiding in him." Our Lord warns us that we shall be separated from him if we fail to meet the serious needs of the poor and the little ones who are his brethren. To die in mortal sin without repenting and accepting God's merciful love means remaining separated from him forever by our own free choice. This state of definitive self-exclusion from communion with God and the blessed is called "hell."[32].

Church Teaching About Evolution

Again, the place to go to discover the authentic teaching of the Church is the Catechism. So, let's look at what it says about the possibility of evolution and, in particular about the rise of human beings.

> 36. For these reasons the Teaching Authority of the Church does not forbid that, in conformity with the present state of human sciences and sacred theology, research and discussions, on the part of men experienced in both fields, take place with regard to the doctrine of evolution, in as far as it inquires into the origin of the human body as coming from pre-existent and living matter—for the Catholic faith obliges us to hold that souls are immediately created by God.[33]

Indeed, not only is it permissible to investigate the origins of the human species, the Church teaches us that doing so will open our eyes to an even greater awe and wonder about our Creator. This is, of course, the central theme of this book. Nothing really new here; it is what the Church teaches us. I am just coming along afterward trying to pull pieces of evidence together to shed further light on the Church's teaching. So, here then is what the Church teaches us:

> 283 The question about the origins of the world and of man has been the object of

> many scientific studies which have splendidly enriched our knowledge of the age and dimensions of the cosmos, the development of life-forms and the appearance of man. These discoveries invite us to even greater admiration for the greatness of the Creator, prompting us to give him thanks for all his works and for the understanding and wisdom he gives to scholars and researchers. With Solomon they can say: "It is he who gave me unerring knowledge of what exists, to know the structure of the world and the activity of the elements for wisdom, the fashioner of all things, taught me.[34]

Further, it is not considered proper by the Church to base our understanding of Creation on a literal interpretation of the Book of Genesis. Cardinal Schönborn explained this point as follows:

> Creationism, based on strictly literal reading of Genesis does not conform to Catholic teaching. The Catholic position on this is clear. St. Thomas says that "One should not try to defend the Christian faith with arguments that are so patently opposed to reason that the faith is made to look ridiculous." It is simply nonsense to say that the world is only 6000 years old. To try to prove this scientifically is what St. Thomas calls provoking the "*irrisio infidelium*," the scorn of the unbelievers. It is not right to use such false arguments and to expose the faith to the scorn of unbelievers.[35]

Figure 13 St. Thomas Aquinas

"One should not try to defend the Christian faith with arguments that are so patently opposed to reason that the faith is made to look ridiculous."

Symbolism of Numbers

Numbers in the Bible in addition to providing relative quantities, though not necessarily exact, frequently carry additional symbolic meanings. If taken literally, quite often, Biblical numbers can lead to misleading conclusions. However, understanding the symbolism associated with certain numbers and combinations of numbers can greatly increase our depth of understanding of the religious and moral teachings of the Bible. Let us look at a few examples.

- Three is the number of the Blessed Trinity. It is the Divine number.[36] It represents the action of God. Jesus' three days in the tomb, in addition to being a count of days, also symbolizes the Divine nature of the Resurrection; the Resurrection is the work of God.
- Four symbolizes the material world. In ancient time, the universe was thought to consist of four elements, earth, fire, water, and air.[37] It represents the physical world as we know it.
- If you multiply the numbers three and four together, you arrive at twelve, another important number with significant symbolism. Since it brings together the Divine and the material, all of the universe, all material things created by the action of God, are symbolized. "It consequently betokens the penetration of matter with spirit."[38] Thus, there were twelve tribes of Israel, God bringing His love and salvation to a symbolic complete material world. This number reaches its perfection in Our Lord's call of the Twelve Apostles, uniting the symbolism of the Twelve Tribes with the universal message of Good News through the salvation brought by the Lord.
- Likewise, if you add the numbers three and four together, you arrive at seven symbolizing again the complete penetration of the material by the Divine. It represents completeness of Divine action in a material world. Thus, Creation was symbolically completed in seven days, the perfectly Divine period of time for God to create every material object in existence. We also see numerous examples of groups of seven relating perfection of the Divine with the material. For example, there are [39]seven sacraments, seven gifts of the Holy Spirit, seven virtues and seven deadly sins.
- Forty is another important number. Forty comes from the multiplication of four (the number for the material world, all of creation) and ten (the number for completeness of humanity). Typically the number forty represents a time of testing or preparation.[40] Dr. Scott Hahn points this out in his commentary on Acts 9:1-19:

> Forty days: A period of final instruction between Easter Sunday and Ascension Thursday. The number 40 signifies a time of preparation for the disciples, just as

Jesus underwent 40 days of preparation before his own ministry. (Matthew 4:2).41

This period of 40 days or years of testing or preparation is linked to:

- The Great Flood of Noah (Genesis 7:4, 17)
- Moses' fast on Mt. Sinai (Exodus34:28)
- Israel's journey in the desert (Deuteronomy 8:2)
- Twelve spies' inspection of Canaan (Numbers 14:34)
- Israel's oppression by the Philistines (Judges 13:1)
- Elijah's fasting (1 Kings 19:8)
- Nineveh's opportunity to repent in response to the preaching of Jonah (Jonah 3:4).

An understanding of the symbolism of numbers significantly helps relate events of the natural world to descriptions of those same events in the Bible. With this understanding, and looking "through the eyes of faith," we see the sacred authors writing about real events in nature in terms they understood, yet with the guidance of the Holy Spirit conveying inerrantly the moral significance and message of faith.

Relating the spiritual symbolism of these numbers, we can relate them to other great events of natural history described in the Bible. Even though we may see natural causes for these events, "through the eyes of faith," we can see the hand of God is no less present as the ultimate cause of them. The Bible certainly could have presented the Creation act of God as a single event occurring at His spoken Word: *Poof! And all creation existed.*

Indeed, for many centuries, scientists believed the universe was static. As it was, it had always been. In 1959, a survey of leading astronomers and physicists asked for their estimate of the age of the universe. Two thirds, certainly a consensus by any standard, had the same answer: It has no age, it has always existed.[42]

But, the Bible presents Creation as a process occurring over a period of time. The seven days is symbolic of the divine and the created coming together in perfection. In fairly recent decades, science has come around to a similar view of a Creation process.

Relative Time

Gerald Schroeder is a physicist, educated at Massachusetts Institute of Technology where he became a professor. He is now a Jewish scholar at the Weizmann Institute in Israel. Dr. Schroeder has written extensively about the scientific accuracy of the Bible. In his book, *The Science of God*, and, his audio version of *Genesis and the Big Bang*, he applies Einstein's Theory of Relativity to the Six Days of Creation as described in Genesis.

Immediately after the Big Bang, the universe, which at this moment consisted entirely of energy[43], expanded at a rate that exceeded the Laws of Physics as we now know them. In this expansion, which lasted only a fraction of a second—perhaps only 0.00001 seconds (10^{-5} seconds), the universe expanded from a singularity of zero dimensions to the size of our solar system.[44] This is called the Inflation.[45][46] Pause for a moment to ponder the significance of the Inflation. On average, it takes light from the Sun something less than eight and a half minutes to reach the Earth. However, Earth is only the third planet from the Sun. Neptune, the farthest planet from the Sun, now that Pluto has been demoted from planetary rank, is approximately 2.8 million miles from the Sun and sunlight takes a little over four hours to reach it. Yet, during the Inflation, the entire universe expanded to the size of the solar system, all the way out to Neptune, in a hundred thousandth of a second. That is more than one billion times the speed of light! After the Inflation, the rate of expansion slowed to its current rate. One reason for the slowing of the expansion of the universe was the appearance of matter. Matter cannot travel at speeds greater than the speed of light. At the instant of the Big Bang, only energy was produced, no matter.[47] As the universe expanded, it cooled until it reached the temperature at which quarks, the building blocks of protons and neutrons, could no longer form from energy and coalesced into protons and neutrons. This temperature is approximately 10.9×10^{12} degrees Kelvin and is known as the Quark Confinement.[48] This is a crucial moment from which we can calculate time from the Big Bang to the present by the ratio of the temperature of Quark Confinement to the present Cosmic Background Temperature of 2.73 degrees Kelvin, a ratio of 4.0×10^{12}.

In Genesis, we read of the initial moments of Creation:

The earth was a formless wasteland. Genesis 1:2.

The Hebrew words translated "formless wasteland" are *tohu* and *bohu*. "The earth was unformed (*tohu*) and void (*bohu*)."[49] But, according to the Jewish Talmud, the Jewish Oral Law redacted circa 500 AD, and the 13th century Jewish Biblical commentator Rabbi Moses Nahmanides, *bohu* also means filled with the building blocks of matter.[50]

The expansion, however, is very important because time is affected by relative position in an expanding universe. To explain, if you were sitting at the origin of the universe at the moment of Creation, and you had a laser that you flashed every second toward the point where the Earth would be 15 billion years later, the time between flashes seen from the Earth would be much greater than the one second interval. If your brother were riding the edge of the expansion of the universe, watching for the flashes of your laser, he would see the first flash in one second. When the universe doubled in size, it would take two seconds for the second flash to reach him. When it doubled again, it would now take four seconds to reach him. This would continue for each doubling of the size of the universe. Therefore, depending on your relative position, the interval between laser flashes would be either one second at the origin, or an exponentially increasing interval between flashes: 1, 2, 4, 8, 16, etc. seconds at the edge of the universe.

The Bible tells us that Creation took place over a period of six days, and then on the seventh day, God rested. Looking closely at the Bible we will see three distinct "creation" events interspersed with several "making" events described in Genesis. The difference being that God "creates" out of nothing and "makes" out of pre-existing materials that He has previously created. The first creation event is the Creation of the universe out of nothing:

> **In the beginning, when God created the heavens and the earth.**

Genesis 1:1.

All of the other events of the six days of Creation describe God "making" things from what He has already created and from which the processes of nature will proceed as they continue to this day. God "made" the sky and the waters on the second day:

> **God made the dome, and it separated the water above the dome from the water below it.**

Genesis 1:7.

The third day, God gathered the waters into a single basin so that dry land appeared and had the Earth bring forth vegetation, all from things he had already created. In effect He is shaping the world in preparation for the man.

> **Then God said, "Let the water under the sky be gathered into a single basin, so that the dry land may appear." And so it happened: the water under the sky was gathered into its basin, and the dry land appeared....**
> **Then God said, "Let the earth bring forth vegetation: every kind of plant that bears seed and every kind of fruit tree on earth that bears fruit with its seed in it." And so it happened: the earth brought forth every kind of plant that bears seed and every kind of fruit tree on earth that bears fruit with its seed in it.**

Genesis 1:9, 11-12.

The fourth day, God "made" the sun, moon, and stars, again, for previously created matter.

> **God made the two great lights, the greater one to govern the day, and the lesser one to govern the night; and he made the stars.**

Genesis 1:16.

The second creation event occurs on the fifth day when God creates life, that common thread of being that is present in all living things. In the Hebrew, this soul of animal life is called the *nefesh*.[51] Note that the *nefesh* was created by God out of nothing. Until that moment, no living animal had existed.

> **Then God said, "Let the water teem with an abundance of living creatures, and on the earth let birds fly beneath the dome of the sky." And so it happened: God created the great sea monsters and all kinds of swimming creatures with which the water teems, and all kinds of winged birds.**

Genesis 1:20-21.

The sixth day, God again made land animals from things which He had previously created including the *nefesh*:

> **God made all kinds of wild animals, all kinds of cattle, and all kinds of creeping things of the earth.**

Genesis 1:25.

Also, on the sixth day, the third and final creation out of nothing was the soul of man. That unique image of God and gift of free will that man alone possesses in Hebrew is called the *neshema*.[52]

> **God created man in his image; in the divine image he created him; male and female he created them.**

Genesis 1:27.

It is important to note that creation of the soul of man reverses the process He has used throughout the Six Days of Creation. In all of the other "creating" and "making" events, God has "created" first, then formed, made, or brought forth from the materials He had created. But, with the creation of man, man is first formed out of pre-existing material, clay; or even pre-existing hominid creatures, and then God breathed His spirit into him, creating in him his *neshema*, his soul, or his spirit.

> **The LORD God formed man out of the clay of the ground and blew into his nostrils the breath of life, and so man became a living being.**

Genesis 2:7.

Looking again at the Six Days of Creation, the plain text of the Bible and the ancient commentaries "definitively state that the Six Days of Genesis were twenty-four hours each, the total duration of which was 'as the six days of our work week.'"[53] But we must keep in mind that this time perspective is from God looking forward from Creation, not from us looking back from the present to the time of Creation; hence the term relative time.

Now, consider our flashing laser from the beginning of this chapter, but instead of flashing the laser every second, it is flashed once every 24 hours according to the Genesis day. Knowing that the ratio of temperatures from the time of Quark Confinement to the present day is approximately 10^{12}, as a measure of the rate of expansion of the universe, using a small amount of calculus, we can calculate the duration of each Genesis day. Dr. Schroeder has described this in detail in his book, *The Science of God*.

The result of Dr. Schroeder's calculation of the duration of each Genesis 24 hour day, seen from the relative perspective of the present looking backwards in time, is as follows:

- Day one ➔ 8 billion years
- Second day ➔ 4 billion years
- Third day ➔ 2 billion years
- Fourth day ➔ 1 billion years
- Fifth day ➔ 500 million years
- Sixth day ➔ 250 million years

The sum of the Six Days of Creation in Genesis relative to today is 15.75 billion years. This is well within the range of recent scientific estimates. Cosmologists and physicists measure the age of the universe to be 10 to 20 billion years old.[54, 55, 56]

Most astonishing is the matchup of events of each Biblical day with corresponding events in scientific literature today. In listing the six days of Creation above, notice I began with Day One, and proceeded to the Second Day, Third Day, etc. This was no oversight, but in keeping with ancient Jewish commentaries by Rabbi Moses Nahmanides in the 13th Century, quoting an even earlier 7th Century commentary. They focus on this description from scripture:

> **...and there was evening and morning, day one.**

Genesis 1:5.

As Dr. Schroeder observed:

> It is not stated "the first day." For the use of *first* would have implied an already existing series of days or a continuation of time when in fact on this "day one" there had been no prior time to this one day...For all remaining days in that week of Genesis, the ordinal terms second, third, etc. are used, and rightly so.[57]

The Genesis Days

Day One
15.75—7.75 Billion Years Ago

> **In the beginning, when God created the heavens and the earth... Then God said, "Let there be light," and there was light.**

Genesis 1:1, 3.

About 14.7 billion years ago, the universe was created in the Big Bang; *see* Figure 14. As one scholar described it, "From the energy of creation, all matter that ever was or will be formed."[58]

Figure 14 The Big Bang

Second Day
7.75—3.75 Billion Years Ago

> **Then God said, "Let there be a dome in the middle of the waters, to separate one body of water from the other." And so it happened: God made the dome, and it separated the water above the dome from the water below it. God called the dome "the sky." Evening came, and morning followed—the second day.**

Genesis 1:5-8.

4.6 billion years ago, the solar system that formed as a cloud of gaseous material began to coalesce, *see* Figure 15.

In approximately 200 million years (4.4 billion years ago), the Earth was formed, but in a molten state, and thus wholly inhospitable to terrestrial life.

About 4.5 billion years ago, the Moon was formed from debris caused by a planet sized object colliding with the Earth. Not only was the Moon formed, but the Earth was given its initial spin, separating day from night.

An additional effect of the Moon forming collision was the creation of a gigantic basin into which the waters of the Earth could collect and be separated from the land. Note that this event was necessary so that dry land would appear.

Figure 15 Dome of the sky

Third Day
3.75—1.75 billion years ago

> **Then God said, "Let the earth bring forth vegetation: every kind of plant that bears seed and every kind of fruit tree on earth that bears fruit with its seed in it." And so it happened: the earth brought forth every kind of plant that bears seed and every kind of fruit tree on earth that bears fruit with its seed in it. God saw how good it was.**

Genesis 1:11-12.

The first living things on Earth were anaerobic bacteria, appearing about 3.5 billion years ago. Note that for 3.2 billion years, these one-celled organisms did not evolve or significantly change.[59]

The process was different, but, like plants and trees today, the bacteria produced oxygen as waste, paving the way for animal life. From this bacteria, both plant and animal life would develop, *see* Figure 16. Note the development of plant life from bacteria to fruit trees, a process covering from 3.8 billion to 120 million years ago.[60]

Figure 16 Appearance of life

Fourth Day
1.75 billion—750 million years ago

> **Then God said: "Let there be lights in the dome of the sky, to separate day from night. Let them mark the fixed times, the days and the years, and serve as luminaries in the dome of the sky, to shed light upon the earth." And so it happened: God made the two great lights, the greater one to govern the day, and the lesser one to govern the night; and he made the stars. God set them in the dome of the sky, to shed light upon the earth, to govern the day and the night, and to separate the light from the darkness. God saw how good it was.**

Genesis 1:14-18.

It might appear that the making of the Sun, Moon, and stars is out of place in the Biblical description because they had all been formed during the Second Day events of the forming of the stars, galaxies (including our own Milky Way), and the solar system including the Earth and Moon. But the atmosphere of the

Earth during the Third and Fourth Days was not at all what we are familiar and comfortable with today. Bill Bryson describes it in his book, *A Short History of Nearly Everything*, as follows:

> If you were to step from a time machine into that ancient Archaean world, you would very swiftly scamper back inside, for there was no more oxygen to breathe on Earth then than there is on Mars today. It was also full of noxious vapors from hydrochloric and sulfuric acids powerful enough to eat through clothing and blister skin. Nor would it have provided the clean and glowing vistas depicted in the poster in Victoria Bennett's office. The chemical stew that was the atmosphere then would have allowed little sunlight to reach the Earth's surface.[61]

In other words, the stars, Sun, and Moon would have all been present from the Second Day, but they could not be seen through the primordial atmosphere. However, the oxygen producing bacteria that appeared in the Third Day were gradually, very gradually clarifying the atmosphere throughout the Fourth Day, so that the celestial bodies became visible. Constant darkness was separated into day and night, as the Earth rotated on its axis, *see* Figure17.

Figure 17 The Atmosphere clears

Fifth Day
750 million—250 million years ago

> **Then God said, "Let the water teem with an abundance of living creatures, and on the earth let birds fly beneath the dome of the sky." And so it happened: God created the great sea monsters and all kinds of swimming creatures with which the water teems, and all kinds of winged birds. God saw how good it was, and God blessed them, saying, "Be fertile, multiply, and fill the water of the seas; and let the birds multiply on the earth."**

Genesis 1:20-22.

About 530 million years ago an event known as the Cambrian Explosion occurred.

The fossil record reveals the sudden, explosive appearance of the first animal life as it flourished in the oceans, 530 million years ago, simultaneously bringing into being all basic body plans of modern life. Then approximately 360 million years ago in rapid succession amphibian reptiles and winged (insect) life appeared.[62]

Note that animal life begins in the sea just as current scientific theories propose. From the sea comes every living creature; *see* Figure 18. Some will remain in the sea and some will venture onto land. You may wonder, as I did, why the birds were included in the same Creation event as the creatures of the sea. The Hebrew word is *oaf*, which means winged animal, which could, of course, mean bird; but the normal Hebrew word for bird is *tsepoor* as found in Genesis 7:3. However, the winged animal meant by *oaf* could also be winged insects[63] which begin their lives as nymphs, an aquatic larval stage. Large dragonfly like insects, such as Meganeura, with wingspans up to 25.6 inches lived in the Carboniferous period, 300 million years ago.

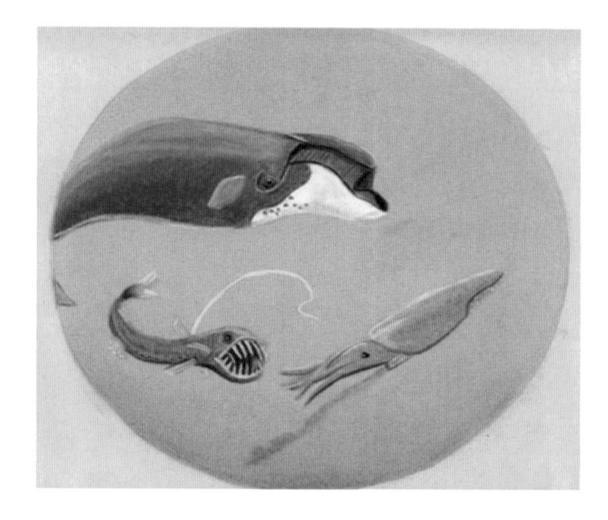

Figure 18 Sea creatures

Sixth Day
250 million—6000 years ago

> **Then God said, "Let the earth bring forth all kinds of living creatures: cattle, creeping things, and wild animals of all kinds." And so it happened: God made all kinds of wild animals, all kinds of cattle, and all kinds of creeping things of the**

earth. God saw how good it was. Then God said: "Let us make man in our image, after our likeness. Let them have dominion over the fish of the sea, the birds of the air, and the cattle, and over all the wild animals and all the creatures that crawl on the ground." God created man in his image; in the divine image he created him; male and female he created them. God blessed them, saying: "Be fertile and multiply; fill the earth and subdue it. Have dominion over the fish of the sea, the birds of the air, and all the living things that move on the earth." Genesis 1:24-28.

250 million years ago there was a mass extinction of animal life both on land and in the sea. 90 to 95 percent of all marine life disappeared from the fossil record.[64] This mass extinction was followed a by repopulation of animal life on land, leading to mammals, hominids, and, finally, man, *see* Figure 19.

Moses told the Israelites,

> **Think back on the days of old,**
> **reflect on the years of age upon age.**

Deuteronomy 32:7.

The end of the Sixth Day represents the division of Biblical time from the Six Days of Creation to the years and ages of Biblical human history.

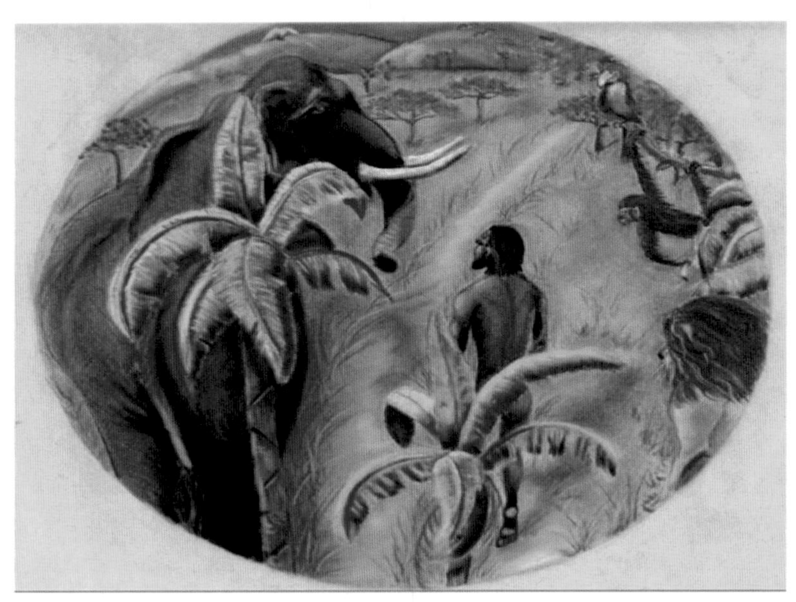

Figure 19 Animal Life

ORAL TRADITION

As a general rule when we pick up the Bible, we don't give much thought to its origins or how the many stories with so many vivid details came to be recorded. Perhaps, the New Testament is easier because, in terms of human existence, it is fairly modern. But, consider some of the Old Testament stories, particularly in the book of Genesis.

Begin with a few facts about the history of writing. Mankind has been creating stories written in pictures since at least 30,000 years BC. These early forms of picture writing evolved over centuries to Sumerian pictographic writing as early as 3500 BC and Egyptian hieroglyphics around 3000 BC. By 2800 BC, the Sumerian picture writing had evolved into wedge shaped symbols, which had spread throughout the Near East by 2500 BC. Sequential pictographic inscriptions, considered to be a true system of writing, did not appear until about 2000 BC. Beginning about 1100 BC, the Phoenicians spread a precursor of a modern alphabet across the Mediterranean Sea to Greece where a modern alphabet with vowels was invented about 800 BC.[65]

Some of the Dead Sea Scrolls discovered at Qumran were written in Paleo-Hebrew dating to the 10th Century BC.[66] Paleo-Hebrew is identical to the Phoenician alphabet. In the 5th Century BC, the Jews adopted the Aramaic alphabet from which the modern Hebrew alphabet evolved although, Paleo-Hebrew continued in use as late as 135 AD.[67]

Now, juxtapose this brief history of writing with some dates along the Biblical time line. If we accept the earliest Paleo-Hebrew writing as sometime during the 10th Century BC (defined as between 1000 BC and 901 BC), this would place the earliest Hebrew writing beginning sometime during the lifetimes of the Prophet

Samuel (born approximately 1155 BC), Saul (crowned king approximately 1050 BC), and David who reigned from approximately 1010 BC until 970 BC.[68] From this we can conclude that, with the exception of possible pictographic representation, the earliest written parts of the Old Testament would date from this same Samuel-Saul-David period. Those Dead Sea Scrolls dated to that time frame would, therefore, represent nearly original copies of the first written texts of the Old Testament.

This also leads to the conclusion the stories we read in the Old Testament, at least prior to the Book of Samuel, were handed down orally from generation to generation until being committed to writing beginning sometime in the 10th Century BC. And, indeed, we receive some clues to the validity of that conclusion within the Scriptures themselves. For example we read in the 78th Psalm:

> **I will open my mouth in story, drawing lessons from of old. We have heard them, we know them; our ancestors have recited them to us.**

Psalm 78 2-3.

Given the time frame of the earliest writings of the Old Testament was the 10th Century BC, it is apparent the stories we are so familiar with in the early books of the Old Testament were passed down orally over several thousands of years. Table 1 list some of the dates of Biblical events or people before the beginning of Paleo-Hebrew writing:[69]

Biblical character or event	**Date**
Samson	1120 BC
Joshua begins conquest of Canaan	1406 BC
God appears to Moses to lead the Israelites out of Egypt	1446 BC
Birth of Moses	1571 BC
Death of Joseph	1836 BC
Jacob and his sons go to Egypt	1906 BC
God calls Abram (later Abraham)	2120 BC

Table 1 Biblical characters before Paleo-Hebrew

From God's call of Abram to the beginning of Hebrew writing was more than 1100 years. If you assume an average birth of a first child at 20 years, a generation, that would mean that the story of Abram was passed down over more than 20 generations.

It is important to digress at this point to address the authorship of the Pentateuch, which is attributed to Moses.[70] This discussion of the history of writing compared to Biblical timelines is in no way intended to cast doubt upon the authorship of the Pentateuch by

Moses. It does however support a contention that the initial authorship was, in fact, oral and it was only after the invention of writing that the oral traditions inerrantly passed down through the generations, under the guidance of the Holy Spirit, were transcribed to written form. Although the time frames differ, this is not unlike the spread of the Gospel in New Testament times. Our Lord was born approximately 6 BC.[71] The crucifixion occurred about 30 AD. But, the first Gospel was not written until approximately 70 AD, 40 years later. Indeed, all of the preaching of St. Peter and St. Paul was oral. They were both martyred by 67 AD, 3 years before the first Gospel was written. As the disasters which befell the kingdoms of Judah and Israel in the Old Testament served as a catalyst for committing Old Testament oral traditions to writing; so the martyrdom of the Apostles served as a catalyst for committing the Gospel message to writing.

There is another fact to consider with regard to Moses. Recall that in the Exodus account, Moses was raised in the court of Pharaoh by the daughter of Pharaoh who had found him floating in a basket in the Nile.

> **Pharaoh's daughter said to her, "Take this child and nurse it for me, and I will repay you." The woman therefore took the child and nursed it. When the child grew, she brought him to Pharaoh's daughter, who adopted him as her son and called him Moses; for she said, "I drew him out of the water."**

Exodus 2:9-10.

I think it is highly likely that Moses, raised in the court of Egypt by a daughter of Pharaoh, would have learned to read and write hieroglyphics as depicted in Figure 20, since hieroglyphics had been invented by 3000 BC. It is likely that Moses, who lived around 1500 BC, was probably just about the only literate Hebrew at the time of the Exodus. Indeed, the Scriptures give us clues to support this conclusion.

Figure 20 Young Moses tutored in Pharaoh's court

> **Then the LORD said to Moses, "Write this down in a document as something to be remembered, and recite it in the ears of Joshua."**

Exodus 17:14.

And again in Deuteronomy we read:

> **Write out this song, then, for yourselves. Teach it to the Israelites and have them recite it, so that this song may be a witness for me against the Israelites.**

Deuteronomy 31:19.

Moses probably obeyed the Lord's instructions by writing the Word of God in hieroglyphics. But, notice how he is instructed to pass God's Word on to the Israelites. He is told, "recite it in the ears of Joshua" and "teach it [the song] to the Israelites and have them recite it." This is oral tradition. This is how the stories are recited generation after generation.

They are recited, chanted, and sung. I was initially led into this line of reasoning while watching the movie, *Jacob and Joseph.* In this movie, Jacob is about to send Joseph out to his brothers wearing his coat of many colors. As he is about to go, Jacob says to him that the reason he loves Joseph best is that he has learned the chants. William Barclay, in his commentary on the genealogy of Jesus in the first chapter of the Gospel of St. Matthew makes the following comment:

> It is further to be noted that this pedigree is most carefully arranged. It is arranged in three groups of fourteen people each. It is in fact what is technically known as a mnemonic, that is to say a thing so arranged that it is easy to memorize.[72]

In my own experience, I recall taking my children to the Space and Rocket Museum in Huntsville, Alabama. In the exhibit on the solar system, there was a song being played over and over again. The song was to the tune of Stephen Foster's *Suwannee River* and the lyrics were, "My very educated mother just sent us nine pizza-pies." This was a mnemonic where the first letter of each word corresponds to the first letter of the planets in order from the Sun. I admit the song loses a bit of its flavor now that Pluto has been demoted from planet status, but at the time, 30 years ago, it was an easy way for us to remember the order of the planets. To this day we, our children, and our grandchildren remember the order of the planets from this simple ditty. My daughter has carried this approach many steps further. She has taught each of her five, home-schooled children a song that names each of the fifty states and its capital. All her children know these useful facts from that song. This is oral tradition in the secular world. Useful information passed along from generation to generation, by song, poem, or repeated repetition.

In addition, there are the stories my mother told us, her children, and we have dutifully passed it on to our children and grandchildren the story of her great grandfather.

Francis Sine's father, Jacob, came to America from Holland with his family. One of Jacob's brothers was a blacksmith in Germantown, Pennsylvania. George Washington often had his horses shod there.

I have not been able to verify the story

except for the fact that Jacob Sine lived in Germantown, Pennsylvania in the early 1800s. Therefore, this story passed along from generation to generation is more than 200 years old. It is a far cry from the stories passed down for millennia that ultimately became written into the Bible. But this is how these stories were passed along.

In the days before, television, multimedia, and even the written word, these Stone Age people would sit around campfires retelling these ancient stories, teaching them to their children and grandchildren, just as Michele Giannetti has so artfully captured in Figure 21.

I would like to pause for a moment to repeat a phrase from a few paragraphs earlier: "Paleo-Hebrew is identical to the Paxhoenician alphabet."

Figure 21 Stone Age storyteller

This is the beginning of the Hebrew writing during the 10th Century BC. It is useful here, to connect some dots with some other facts at our disposal coming from the Holy Scriptures. King Solomon reigned in the united Kingdom of Israel from approximately 970 BC to approximately 931 BC. That would be during the 10th Century BC. During that time, Solomon formed a treaty with King Hiram of Tyre, a Phoenician city.

> **The LORD, moreover, gave Solomon wisdom as he promised him, and there was peace between Hiram and Solomon, since they were parties to a treaty.**

1 Kings 5:26.

Hiram and Solomon had numerous business arrangements including acquiring materials and craftsmen for the Temple and a fleet of ships that brought gold, fine wood, and precious stones.

> **Hiram's fleet, which used to bring gold from Ophir, also brought from there a large quantity of cabinet wood and precious stones. The king had a fleet of Tarshish ships at sea with Hiram's fleet. Once every three years the fleet of Tarshish ships would come with a cargo of gold, silver, ivory, apes, and monkeys.**

1 Kings 10:11, 22.

Aside from his business dealings amassing great wealth for the Kingdom of Israel, Solomon is also known for his great wisdom.

> **Men came to hear Solomon's wisdom from all nations, sent by all the kings of the earth who had heard of his wisdom.**

1 Kings 5:14.

It is entirely likely that some of the wisdom that Solomon knew and preserved in written form was nothing less than the oral traditions of Israel which would become parts of the Old Testament. Indeed, many of the Dead Sea Scrolls are copies written in the very Paleo-Hebrew script, which Solomon would likely have acquired from his association with King Hiram of Tyre. Although it is recognized that these are not original texts from the time of Solomon, they are probably copies of earlier Paleo-Hebrew texts, which may stretch back to Solomon's time. The texts of some of these scrolls written in Paleo-Hebrew include the following:

- 4QpaleoGen
- 11Q1 Leviticus
- 4Q22 Exodus
- 4QpaleoJob
- 11Q5 Psalms

One would think that the Psalms would have been of particular interest to Solomon because many of them had been composed by his father, King David.

Although parts of the Old Testament may have been committed to writing as early as the time of Solomon, at least some scholars reckon the first editing occurred during the reign of King Josiah of Judah who ruled 639-609 BC, but the final editing occurred during the exile in Babylon or shortly after.[73] The exile in Babylon began with the conquest of Judah by Babylon in 586 BC, and lasted until the 536 BC decree of the Persian, King Cyrus, who had conquered Babylon and permitted the people of Israel to return to the Promised Land and restore Jerusalem and the Temple.[74]

The point of the discussion of the dates of writing the Old Testament as being during a period from approximately 1000 to 500 BC is to recognize the role of oral traditions in the development of this monument to our salvation history. As we have seen, Abraham lived more than a thousand years before the written form of the Old Testament. As we shall see later in this book, Noah may have lived some 12,000 or even 40,000 years earlier, and the stories of Adam and Eve and Cain and Abel may well go back as much as 150,000 years earlier. I realize that these numbers may seem incredible, but I will provide the scientific data that supports this hypothesis and my firm belief that these were real people whose stories we tell. And that is the crux of the argument: the stories we tell. This 150,000 years of human activity in our salvation history was preserved and passed down from generation to generation over this entire period of time.

Consider Abraham who lived around 2100 BC. He was a shepherd. He made a living for himself and a growing family by tending sheep and goats. He had no way of preserving his story except by word of mouth. Although, Abraham lived in the Late Stone Age to Early Bronze Age, technology did not advance evenly or as rapidly as in the modern era. Even in the time of Joshua, a thousand years after Abraham, knives of flint were still being used.

> **So Joshua made flint knives and circumcised the Israelites.**

Joshua 5:3.

They were still Stone Age people. They had no other means of passing on their stories or their history. It would more than a thousand years until the invention of even the most ancient forms of Hebrew writing. Amihai Mazar, an archeologist from the Hebrew University of Jerusalem, had the following to say about the written forms of oral tradition in the Scriptures:

> I recognize that the Pentateuch, the collection that scholars call the "Deuteronomist History," consisting of Deuteronomy, Joshua, Judges, Samuel, and Kings, as well as large parts of the prophetic and wisdom literature, were written and further edited during the late Monarchy (eighth—early sixth centuries B.C.E.) and even later, during the Babylonian Exile and the Persian period that followed (sixth—fourth centuries B.C.E.). But I also accept the view of many scholars that the late monarchic

> authors and editors used early materials such as Temple and palace libraries and archives, monumental inscriptions perhaps centuries old, oral transmissions of poetry, folk stories rooted in a remote historical past, and perhaps even some earlier historiographic writings.[75]

One of the characteristics of oral traditions is that occasionally small variances occur in the retelling. Consider the Twelve Tribes of Israel, each passing along these oral traditions. It is to be expected that variations will occur. What is surprising is that when these stories were committed to written form, there was no apparent attempt to reconcile these variations. Both stories are told, but the theological message remains the same. For example, in Genesis chapters 6 and 7, there are two slightly differing descriptions of the animals Noah was directed to take into the Ark.

> **Of all other living creatures you shall bring two into the ark, one male and one female, that you may keep them alive with you.**

Genesis 6:19.

> **Of every clean animal, take with you seven pairs, a male and its mate; and of the unclean animals, one pair, a male and its mate.**

Genesis 7:2.

The stories differ slightly, but the theological message remains unchanged. Another characteristic of oral traditions is that events are not always described in chronological order. I am reminded of sitting around with a group of veterans telling their war stories. Anyone taking notes to later record these stories would have to recall the stories told will not be in chronological sequence. One story will engender the telling of another related story, while another will go off on a different tangent altogether with no thought for chronology. Consider the plight of the sacred writer putting together all these separate stories given to him in random sequence and making a coherent story.

One of the characteristics of our written Bible is that it was not written by a single author at one time and place. In addition, the human authors used numerous literary techniques and genres to preserve the sacred message. The Catechism prepares us to appreciate literary styles in our study of Sacred Scripture:

> 110 In order to discover the sacred authors' intention, the reader must take into account the conditions of their time and culture, the literary genres in use at that time, and the modes of feeling, speaking and narrating then current. "For the fact is that truth is differently presented and expressed in the various types of historical writing, in prophetical and poetical texts, and in other forms of literary expression."[76]

For example, in the book of Numbers there is a fable inserted into the narrative of a story.

Before proceeding, consider what a fable is. It is a short tale, often including talking animals, used to impart a moral or characteristic of life. For example, one of Aesop's fables concerns a fox trying to reach some grapes hanging far above his head. When he finally gave up in frustration, the fox wandered away muttering, "The grapes were probably sour anyway." It is from this fable that we derive the expression, "sour grapes." In the Numbers story, the prophet Balaam has been hired by the King of Moab to call down a curse upon the Israelites as they complete their forty years wandering in the wilderness. Balaam says he can only say what the Lord tells him to say, and throughout this episode remains true to that guidance. The story begins:

> **"I will reward you very handsomely and will do anything you ask of me. Please come and lay a curse on this people for me." But Balaam replied to Balak's officials, "Even if Balak gave me his house full of silver and gold, I could not do anything, small or great, contrary to the command of the LORD, my God. But, you too shall stay here overnight, till I learn what else the LORD may tell me." That night God came to Balaam and said to him, "If these men have come to summon you, you may go with them; yet only on the condition that you do exactly as I tell you."**

Numbers 22:17-20.

Note that at this point, the Lord has given Balaam permission to accompany the officials back to the King of Moab. There is no indication Balaam will say anything contrary to the Lord's instructions. But, then comes the inserted fable:

> **So the next morning when Balaam arose, he saddled his ass, and went off with the princes of Moab. But now the anger of God flared up at him for going, and the angel of the LORD stationed himself on the road to hinder him as he was riding along on his ass, accompanied by two of his servants. When the ass saw the angel of the LORD standing on the road with sword drawn, she turned off the road and went into the field, and Balaam had to beat her to bring her back on the road. Then the angel of the LORD took his stand in a narrow lane between vineyards with a stone wall on each side. When the ass saw the angel of the LORD there, she shrank against the wall; and since she squeezed Balaam's leg against it, he beat her again. The angel of the LORD then went ahead, and stopped next in a passage so narrow that there was no room to move either to the right or to the left. When the ass saw the angel of**

the LORD there, she cowered under Balaam. So, in anger, he again beat the ass with his stick. But now the LORD opened the mouth of the ass, and she asked Balaam, "What have I done to you that you should beat me these three times?" "You have acted so willfully against me," said Balaam to the ass, "that if I but had a sword at hand, I would kill you here and now." But the ass said to Balaam, "Am I not your own beast, and have you not always ridden upon me until now? Have I been in the habit of treating you this way before?" "No," replied Balaam. Then the LORD removed the veil from Balaam's eyes, so that he too saw the angel of the LORD standing on the road with sword drawn; and he fell on his knees and bowed to the ground. But the angel of the LORD said to him, "Why have you beaten your ass these three times? It is I who have come armed to hinder you because this rash journey of yours is directly opposed to me. When the ass saw me, she turned away from me these three times. If she had not turned away from me, I would have killed you; her I would have spared." Then Balaam said to the angel of the LORD, "I have sinned. Yet I did not know that you stood against me to oppose my journey. Since it has displeased you, I will go back home." But the angel of the LORD said to Balaam, "Go with the men; but you may say only what I tell you." So Balaam went on with the princes of Balak.

Figure 22 Balaam and the angel

Numbers 22:21-35.

Then the story continues as if the fable had not been inserted.

So Balaam went on with the princes of Balak.

Numbers 22:21-35.

The literary genre of the fable reinforces the Lord's admonition to say nothing that God has not revealed to him. Yet if you read the fable in line with the rest of the story, there is an implication of disobedience by Balaam not present without the fable. In fact, the fable is just the type of story that would be told by the tribal storyteller to impress upon his listeners the importance of obedience to the commands of God.

The Most Amazing Book In The World

First and foremost the Bible is the Word of God. Although its authors are human, it is divinely inspired. The authors wrote in words and ideas which they could understand to convey a message authentically from God. Dr. Scott Hahn describes it as follows:

> The Holy Spirit enlightened the intellects of many different specific authors over thousands of years so they could conceive all that which God wanted them to write down and nothing more. Divine inspiration infallibly moved the will of each sacred author—without impairing his freedom in any way—to write what was in his intellect. Divine inspiration assisted the human author to use the correct language and expressions to describe what was being infallibly written. This means God is the principle author of Scripture; the human authors are also true authors.[77]

The Bible is written for our instruction. It is not a book of stories, legends, and myths. It is a book of stories about real people and real events, told for a purpose. The purpose is the salvation of humanity. It is to bring the human spirit into harmony and eternal communion with God Himself. We apprehend that purpose when we read and study the Bible as the Church teaches, recognizing the senses of Scripture. We will learn the events that happened over the course of human history from the very beginning of the human species. From these events, we recognize the coming of Our Redeemer, Our Lord and Savior, Jesus Christ. We learn how we are to live in harmony with Our God Who created us—body, soul, and eternal spirit—and with our fellow brothers and sisters. And we learn the destiny God has planned for each of us and which can only be denied to us by our own willful and deliberate refusal to accept that eternity with God.

The Bible is not a Book of Science or History

The Bible is not a scientific book, nor is it a history book in the usual sense. It was not composed as an erudite report after an extensive archeological expedition. It does not propose hypotheses, challenging them with carefully measured observations supported by mathematical analysis. As a book of history, it does not even tell the events in chronological order. Measured by the rigorous standards of scholarly research, it would undoubtedly be a failure. Of course, that is not its purpose. It pronounces facts, not that we can examine and verify, but facts from the very Mind of God. The facts are not given for us to study and compare with other facts so that we may build a logical case reaching an orderly conclusion. They are simply facts from God teaching us how to live with each other in peace and harmony and how to live in the presence of our God. The Prophet Micah very succinctly summarizes the whole purpose of the Bible:

> **You have been told, O man, what is good, and what the LORD requires of you: Only to do right and to love goodness, and to walk humbly with your God.**

Micah 6:8.

If we live by these words, not only will we have peace in our lives, but we will answer the beckoning of our God and find Jesus in our lives. And where will we find Him? We will find Him exactly where he told us we would find Him.

> **Did you not know that I must be in my Father's house?**

Luke 2:49.

We will find Him in the Church that He established on this Earth, beginning with Adam and Eve, continuing through Father Abraham, leading right up to Our Lord Himself, and continuing through His Apostles and their successors to this very day. And it is that Church that has kept His Holy Word throughout the centuries and millennia. The Church has kept it for our instruction to bring us ever closer to Him.

I began this section with the statement that "The Bible is not a book of science or history." For certain, that is not its purpose. But, the simple fact is that the Bible is a book of history and of science; not by means of what today we call the scientific method, but by means of the spoken word brought forward over tens of thousands of years until it could be written and preserved in print. It tells us through the lives of living people the most significant milestones in the development of the human person from preexisting hominid creatures. It will tell in these stories things that were beyond the understanding of primitive man, even at times to modern day man. It tells, for example, that life began in the sea, that plant life appeared first on the dry land, that before our modern fauna there were other creatures to include dinosaurs. It tells of the history of the cosmos from the moment time began, a concept captured in the Bible and understood by Church Fathers, such as St. Augustine, but not understood by modern scientists until the middle 1900s. It captures the formation of the Sun, Moon, stars, and, of course, the Earth with scientific accuracy that is still being revealed to the minds of modern science. The Bible also describes monumental milestones in human development, for example, our original diet was strictly plants, and only later meat did meat become a part of the human diet. It captures the very beginning of this forest living creature adopting the habit of wearing clothes, leather clothes—skins of animals. It marks the discovery of fire and notes that all the animals would fear man. It notes the beginning of agriculture where mankind would no longer subsist on the berries and leaves gathered from their surroundings. We read of waves of migrations out of the original human homeland spreading ever eastward. And it observes the beginnings of cities constructed of mud bricks and the dispersion of languages from an original single mother tongue. It walks through the sweep of ancient human history telling of life throughout the ages of man, the Stone Age, Bronze Age, and Iron Age; of the great clashes of empires and how they affected a small remnant of human beings, a Chosen People. These mighty empires of Egypt, Assyria, and Babylon give way to conquests by the Persian Empire, only to be conquered by the Greeks under Alexander the Great, which in turn falls to the Roman Empire.

In addition, "the Bible is the earliest identifiable source of the great conceptual discoveries essential for civilization: equality before the law, sanctity of life, dignity of the individual, individual and common responsibility, peace as an ideal, love as the foundation of justice."[78] All this is seen through the eyes of this faithful remnant, recorded in their oral traditions, eventually becoming parts of our Holy Scriptures coming down to us today under the guidance of the Holy Spirit.

I recognize these are rather bold assertions; however, I will present the basis for them in the remainder of this book. For now, I will present two examples from the historical perspective that illustrate how we can learn real history from the Bible. Certainly, all faithful Christians, for whom this book is intended, are familiar with the stories of David, human ancestor of Our Lord and King of the undivided Kingdom of Israel and Judah. We know him as the boy who fought the giant Goliath, his trials with Saul, his ultimate kingship, and his failing with Bathsheba. We have a record of conversations, prayers, and introspection. David lived some 3000 years ago and everything we know about him comes from the Bible. Until very recently, there was absolutely no evidence outside the Bible, scientific or historical, that David, Israel's greatest king, ever existed. It was not until 1993 at a site of Tel Dan in northern Israel that a

Figure 23 Tel Dan inscription David Stela

stone slab, a stela, was discovered that provides the first historical evidence of the existence of David. The inscription commemorates an Aramean victory over the "king of Israel" and the House of David.[79] The historical information from the world of science and history is sparse and thin, whereas the history from the Bible is rich, and has been with us for thousands of years. In time, perhaps historians will catch up, but with the 3000 year head start, we may have to be patient.

The second example comes from the time of the Jews' captivity in Babylon after the conquest of Judea and Jerusalem in 597 BC. In 539 BC, Cyrus the Great of Persia conquered the Babylonians. Second Chronicles ends and Ezra begins with the same words:

> **In the first year of Cyrus, king of Persia, in order to fulfill the word of the LORD spoken by Jeremiah, the LORD inspired King Cyrus of Persia to issue this proclamation throughout his kingdom, both by word of mouth and in writing: "Thus says Cyrus, king of Persia: 'All the kingdoms of the earth the LORD, the God of heaven, has given to me, and he has also charged me to build him a house in Jerusalem, which is in Judah. Whoever, therefore, among you belongs to any part of his people, let him go up, and may his God be with him!'" 2 Chronicles 36:22-23; Ezra 1:1-3.**

The Jewish exiles in Babylon were set free to return to Judea and Jerusalem to rebuild the city of Jerusalem and restore the Temple. The trials and efforts of this faithful remnant is recorded in the books of Ezra and Nehemiah. These books are thought by many scholars to have been written sometime before the conquest of Persia by Alexander the Great in 335 BC, or about 200 years after the fall of Babylon and release of the Hebrews. As an aside, which we will return to later, the Greek historian Herodotus also records the fall of Babylon to the Persians.

In 1879, an inscribed clay cylinder was discovered in the ruins of the ancient city of Babylon. The cylinder celebrates the accomplishments of Cyrus the Great and includes a statement that he was "freeing their inhabitants from their "yoke." He repaired the ruined temples in the cities he conquered, restored their cults, and returned their sacred images and their former inhabitants, taken by Narbonidus, to Babylon."[80]

As always, there is wide divergence of opinion among scientists and historians, but many scholars argue these words on the cylinder are confirmation of the release of the Hebrews, among other conquered peoples, to return to their homelands and restore their places of worship. If, as seems likely, this interpretation is correct, it confirms historical events as presented in the Bible.

Figure 24 Cyrus cylinder discovered in 1879

Reliability of the Bible

There is no known original manuscript of even a single book of either the Old Testament or the New Testament. How, then, is it possible to make claims of great reliability, indeed, of inerrancy and infallibility. Although there are no claims of inerrancy and infallibility in secular histories and writings, we have no problems giving them great credence. Thucydides wrote a history of the Peloponnesian War. He lived from 460 -400 BC, concurrent with the events about which he wrote. Almost everything we know about that 27 year war comes from his writings. "Yet, the earliest copy of any manuscripts of Thucydides' work dates around 900 AD, a full 1,300 years later!"[81] Similarly, Herodotus, another ancient Greek historian wrote in the 480—425 BC period. We have only eight manuscripts of his works, the earliest copy is dated approximately 900 AD, again 1300 years after the time of the writing.[82] Likewise, secular writings from the New Testament period are also few in number. "Only 10 copies of the writings of Caesar, along with another 20 copies of the historian Tacitus, and 7 copies from the historian Pliny, who all originally wrote in the first century, are available today."[83]

Comparing the availability of manuscripts

and the age of available manuscripts gives a huge advantage to Biblical sources, both New Testament and Old Testament. There are more than 24,000 copies of New Testament manuscripts with 230 compiled before 600 AD.[84] The table below lists several of the oldest, most significant New Testament manuscripts available today.

Note that for these manuscripts, the time span from the dates they were written to the date of the copy, range from coexistent to 350 years. For the Magdalene manuscript of Matthew 26, coexistent means that the copy was made very soon after the original while the author, disciples, and witnesses . In addition to the manuscripts themselves, the Biblical library includes the writings of numerous fathers of the early Church. So extensive are the quotations of Scripture by these Church fathers that all but eleven verses of the New Testament are accounted for in their writings.[93] The abundance of manuscripts, translations, quotations and other documents means that scholars can make detailed comparisons between the various sources. This analysis shows that less than one half of one percent of the approximately 20,000 lines of the New Testament is in question in the sense of variant reading. Of these, only one eighth are anything more than a stylistic difference or misspelling.[94] More importantly, "not one essential point of Christian doctrine rests upon a disputed reading."[95]

Perhaps, more challenging is the case for the reliability of the Old Testament simply because of the much more ancient sources: oral traditions, in some cases, dating back tens of thousands of years, paleo-Hebew writings dating to the 10th century BC, and the books of the Old Testament written and edited after the

Manuscript	**Date Written**	**Copy Date**	**Time Span Years**	**Note**
Magdalene Manuscript (Matthew 26)	1st century	50-60 AD	co-existent (?)	85
John Rylands (John)	90 AD	130 AD	40	86
Bodmer Papyrus II (John)	90 AD	150-200 AD	60-110	87
Chester Beatty Papyri (N.T.)	1st century	200 AD	150	88
Diatessaron by Tatian (Gospels)	1st century	200 AD	150	89
Codex Vaticanus (Bible)	1st century	325-350 AD	275-300	90
Codex Sinaiticus (Bible)	1st century	350 AD	300	91
Codex Alexandrinus (Bible)	1st century	400 AD	350	92

Table 2 New Testament Manuscripts

return from exile in the mid-6th century BC to the latest books written in Greek during the Hasmonean period in the mid-2nd century BC.

The Israelites had a commandment from God:

> **In your observance of the commandments of the LORD, your God, which I enjoin upon you, you shall not add to what I command you nor subtract from it.**

Deuteronomy 4:2.

Jesus Himself commented on the enduring permanence of the Law:

> **For verily I say unto you, till heaven and earth pass, one jot or one tittle shall in no wise pass from the law, till all be fulfilled.**

Matthew.

A jot was the smallest of Hebrew letters, yod. A tittle was "The smallest part of the letter--what the King James Version calls the tittle--is what we call the serif, the little projecting part at the foot of a letter, the little line at each side of the foot of, for example, the letter "I."[96]

All of this meant that the Jews took exacting care to preserve their written Word unchanged in even the slightest letter or marking.

> Jews preserved it as no other manuscript has ever been preserved. With their massora they kept tabs on every letter, syllable, word and paragraph. They had special classes of men within their culture whose sole duty was to preserve and transmit these documents with practically perfect fidelity ... who ever counted the letters, syllables and words of Plato or Aristotle? Cicero or Seneca? [97]

But, we also have empirical evidence of the accuracy of the Old Testament texts. Prior to the discovery of the Dead Sea Scrolls in 1947, the earliest manuscript of the Book of Isaiah was the Masoretic Text, dating to 900 AD. Among the Dead Sea Scrolls, found in the Qumran Caves Scrolls over a ten year period between 1946 and 1956 near the ancient settlement at Khirbet Qumran in the West Bank, was a copy of Isaiah dating back to 100 BC—a thousand years earlier than the Masoretic Text.

> This scroll, dating to approximately 100 B.C. was found to be identical to the Modern Hebrew Bible in over ninety five percent of the text. The remaining five percent consisted chiefly of obvious slips of the pen or variations in spelling.[98]

This represented more than a thousand years of copying without any appreciable change in the text.[99] Although there is virtually never unanimity among archeologists, two prominent archeologists attest to the archeological and historical accuracy of Biblical texts. Nelson Glueck, renowned Jewish archaeologist, wrote:

> It may be stated categorically that no archaeological discovery has ever controverted a biblical reference." [100]

William F. Albright, one of the world's most renowned archaeologists, stated:

> There can be no doubt that archaeology has confirmed the substantial historicity of Old Testament tradition.[101]

Briefly having addressed, to confirm certain faith, the oral traditions from which the Holy Scripture in written form ultimately derived, the stage is now set to apply our logic and reason to the scientific discoveries and models uncovered by modern science. But, in applying our reason, we shall also see "through the eyes of faith." Together, our reason and faith can give us a new perspective and enable us to answer the question that inspired this book: "What do we tell our children?"

Figure 25 The Great Isaiah Scroll (1Qisa)
Found in one of eleven caves near the ancient settlement at Khirbet Qumran in the West Bank about one and a half miles inland from the Dead Sea

CREATION AND EVOLUTION

In the beginning, when God created the heavens and the earth ... God said, "Let there be light," and there was light.
Genesis 1:1, 3.

For many years, there was a general consensus among scientists that the universe had no beginning; it just was. The universe was considered to be static and without any kind of starting point or event. Then, in 1929 the astronomer, Edwin Hubble, made the discovery that no matter where you looked in the universe, distant galaxies were all moving away from us, suggesting the concept of an abrupt beginning, not only of all the matter in the universe, but of time itself. This abrupt beginning is commonly called the Big Bang.[102] The Big Bang is a scientific model that, for the present, most nearly accounts for the observable phenomena of the universe as we know it. In a concise summary, shown in Figure 26, the Big Bang model posits that all the matter and energy making up the universe came into being instantaneously at a single point of zero size and, therefore, of infinite density. This dimensionless point is called a singularity. At the

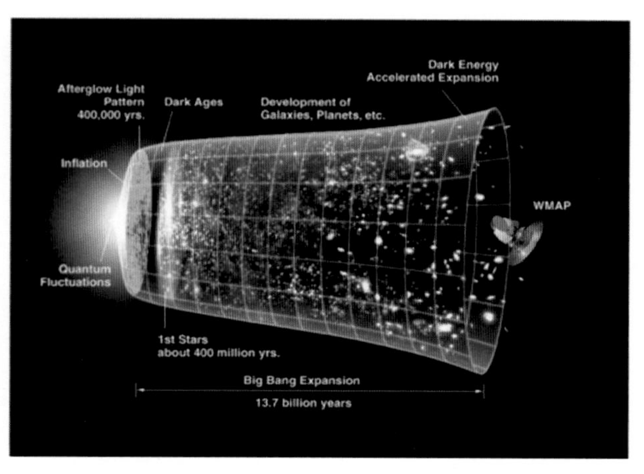

Figure 26 The Big Bang

instant of the appearance of this singularity, it began to expand rapidly.

Allow me to define "rapidly." In 10^{-43} seconds, that is a decimal point followed by 43 zeros and a 1, the universe expanded from zero size to about the size of a softball. By 10^{-32} seconds, all of the matter in the universe consisted of nothing but electrons and subatomic particles called quarks. Quarks are the building blocks of the nucleus of an atom. By 10^{-6} seconds, or one millionth of a second, quarks began to coalesce into protons and neutrons, but had not yet formed into atoms. At 3 minutes after the Big Bang, the universe is continuing to expand rapidly and to cool. Cool, however, is a relative term. At this point the temperature is 100 billion degrees Celsius; much too hot for this seething soup of electrons, protons, and neutrons to form into atoms. It also has too much energy, that is, it is too hot to emit light in the visible spectrum. This state would continue for 300,000 years.

At this point, I would like to digress from the description of the Big Bang, and return to the astonishing words of the Biblical description of the beginning of the Creation process in the Book of Genesis. It is significant to note that the Bible does not say the Creation occurred all at once, in a single instant. As a Catholic Christian I believe in an omnipotent God Who could, if it pleased Him to do so, create the universe exactly as we see it today in a single instant at His Word. It is apparent from science and from the description given to us in the Holy Scriptures, that it did not please Him to do so. Instead, He proceeded with a process for Creation. It was a process that occurred over a period of time, specifically, seven days. However, we must note that quite often, indeed, generally, numbers have a symbolic significance rather than a specific mathematical value in the Bible. In addition to giving a quantity, they also convey a message. In the case of the number seven, it represents completeness. In particular, it represents completeness in a theological sense. Hence, seven days symbolically represents the completeness of God's action in Creation, not a literal quantity of seven twenty four hour periods.

Recognizing that those who began to pass down the oral traditions of the Biblical Creation story and those who much later committed these stories to written form had no way of understanding or even conceiving the creation process presently understood by today's science, except of course, by Divine inspiration. Yet, look again what the words say:

> **In the beginning, when God created the heavens and the earth, the earth was a formless wasteland, and darkness covered the abyss, while a mighty wind swept over the waters.**

Genesis 1:1-2.

In the beginning, God created all of the energy and matter in the universe, indeed, in all universes. (I shall address this thought in a later chapter.) Note what the Genesis passage says about this initial period of time after Creation: "darkness covered the abyss." Look up any modern depiction of the Big Bang, including Figure 26, or any of Dr. Stephen Hawking's books on the universe; they all show a bright explosion. It was not; it was a dark explosion. The Bible got it right.

Precisely as described in the modern Big Bang scientific model, matter and energy come first, followed by the appearance of light. In fact, the Genesis description of the first 300,000 years of Creation is scientifically more accurate than our modern science Big Bang descriptions in a general way! As any eighth grade science teacher can readily demonstrate, if you put an alarm clock in a bell jar and evacuate all the air, there will be no sound from the ringing alarm clock. Sound requires matter to propagate and at the instant of the Big Bang, there was no matter outside the primordial singularity and, therefore, no bang to be heard. Instead, there was merely a burst of energy without sound or light for 300,000 years until God said, "Let there be light." Secondly, the Big Bang was not big at all. In fact, it was infinitesimally small. All of the matter and all of the energy in the entire universe as we know it today was compressed into a space of zero dimensions and infinite density. That is, of course, not big; it is infinitely smaller than the period at the end of this sentence. So the Big Bang was not big, nor was there a bang, nor even a flash of light. We can paraphrase T.S. Eliot's poem about the end of the world, *The Hollow Men* when he says:

> This is the way the world ends
> Not with a bang but a whimper. [103]

It seems the world began, not with a Big Bang, but a whimper.

According to Stephen Hawking, at a singularity such as the Big Bang, where all the matter and energy of the universe is compressed into a dimensionless point, the laws of physics, both Newtonian and relativity, will not hold.[104] However, once the Big Bang began its expansion, one would expect the laws of physics to apply. Another exception to the laws of physics is in the execution of a divine, supernatural miracle. Certainly, the moment of creation would qualify as such a miracle. Let's look at some of the laws of physics that are violated during the creation process, including times when one would expect them to apply.

The Catholic Church teaches that God created the universe out of nothing.

> 296 We believe that God needs no pre-existent thing or any help in order to create, nor is creation any sort of necessary emanation from the divine substance. God creates freely "out of nothing." (Lateran Council IV, 1215)[105]

God simply caused it into being. The Big Bang essentially assumes the same thing. There is no explanation whatsoever that describes the initial existence of matter and energy. One of the fundamental laws of physics, the Conservation of Energy and Matter, is that energy and matter can neither be created nor destroyed, but only changed in form. As Albert Einstein wrote:

> Pre-relativity physics contains two conservation laws of fundamental importance, namely the law of conservation of energy and the law of conservation of mass; these two appear there as completely independent of each other. Through relativity theory they melt together into one principle. [106]

Normal chemical processes such as burning a piece of wood, merely convert the hydrocarbon molecules in a piece of wood into its constituent atoms or other molecules. Every atom that was initially present in the piece of wood is still present as carbon in the ash, carbon dioxide, carbon monoxide, or water vapor in the smoke. Only the form is changed. In a nuclear reaction, a material may be converted into a different isotope (same number of protons, but a different number of neutrons), or a different element if the number of protons is changed, but the differences are made up in energy in accordance with Einstein's equation: $E=Mc^2$. This is precisely what happens in the nuclear fission reaction in a nuclear reactor or when an atomic bomb is detonated, or in a nuclear fusion reaction which is the process for producing energy and light by the Sun depicted by the NASA photograph in Figure 27. In a fusion reaction, two hydrogen atoms fuse to form a single helium atom giving off a tremendous amount of energy in the process.

However, at the moment of Creation, the moment of the Big Bang, all of the energy and matter that would ever exist in the universe was created. It was not changed in form; it was created out of nothing. At that moment, not only did all matter and energy begin its

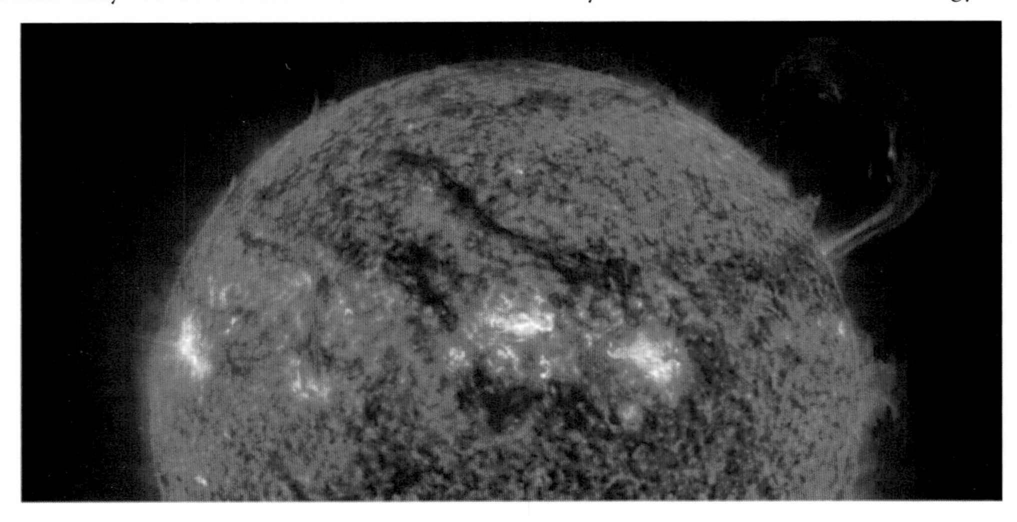

Figure 27 Nuclear fusion energy in the Sun

existence, but time also began. There was neither matter nor energy nor time prior to that moment. This, of course, soundly violates the Law of Conservation of Energy and Matter. It is curious to note that the concept of time, having its beginning at the moment of Creation, was discussed by St. Augustine in *De Genesi*, written near the beginning of the 5th century:

> 338 Nothing exists that does not owe its existence to God the Creator. The world began when God's word drew it out of nothingness; all existent beings, all of nature, and all human history are rooted in this primordial event, the very genesis by which the world was constituted and time begun.[107]

A second law of Newtonian physics that is violated at the moment of Creation is Newton's Third Law: "For every action, there is always opposed an equal reaction."[108] In the Big Bang, there is only the reaction of the explosive expansion of the matter and energy in the primordial singularity. But there is no prior action to initiate it. There is no prior action, because there is "no prior." Since time began at the instant of Creation, nothing could previously move the expansion into motion. Aristotle, who lived in the middle of the 4th century BC envisioned an "Unmoved Mover" that set all of the universe into motion at the moment of Creation. In Christian apologetics, this "Unmoved Mover" is God Himself as St. Thomas Aquinas offers as one of his proofs of the existence of God in "The Argument for Motion" in *Summa Theological*, from the 13th Century. That is God by His own Divine will caused the universe to come into being and time to begin, without any prior movement prodding Him into action.

Scientists have difficulty with these notions because they cannot be observed or measured, so there is no way, even indirectly to calculate what may have preceded the Big Bang. Stephen Hawking, the Nobel laureate cosmologist and theoretical physicist, merely dismisses it because anything that may have happened before the Big Bang can have no influence on anything occurring after the Big Bang. It may simply be ignored.

> If there were events earlier than this time, then they could not affect what happens at the present time. Their existence can be ignored because it would have no observable consequences.[109]

In fact, Dr. Hawking goes on to admit that one reason scientists are uncomfortable with a Big Bang beginning of the universe and time is that it implies the possibility of Divine action which incompatible with the scientific method.

Most people do not like the idea that time has a beginning, probably because it smacks of divine intervention.[110]

In moving from Newtonian physics to the physics of relativity, we also encounter violation of a fundamental law that nothing may travel faster than the speed of light. This law was quantified in Einstein's equation $E=Mc^2$. Stephen Hawking describes the effect of this equation.

> Because of the equivalence of energy and mass, the energy which it has due to its motion will add to its mass....As an object approaches the speed of light, its mass rises ever more quickly, so it takes more and more energy to speed it up further. It can, in fact, never reach the speed of light, because by then its mass would have become infinite, and by the equivalence of mass and energy, it would have taken an infinite amount of energy to get there. For this reason, any normal object is forever confined by relativity to move slower than the speed of light. Only light and other waves that have no intrinsic mass can travel at the speed of light.[111]

However, in the descriptions of the Big Bang, the universe is said to have reached the size of a softball in 10^{-43} seconds and "in less than a minute the universe is a million billion miles across and growing fast."[112] However, both of these descriptions require that the matter within the Big Bang was moving at greater than the speed of light. Even if only energy was present at the initial moments of the Big Bang, it is still limited to the speed of light. To put this into perspective from a closer to home view, the Earth is approximately 93 million miles from the Sun. It takes about 8 minutes for light from the Sun to reach the Earth. That is, by definition, at the speed of light, light travels 93 million miles in 8 minutes. In the first1 minute after the Big Bang, light, matter, and energy had traveled, not 93 million miles, but 1,000,000,000 million miles.

So what can we conclude for all of these violations of fundamental laws? The apparent conclusion seen "through the eyes of faith" is the Creation, the Big Bang, was nothing less than a divine miracle called into being by an omnipotent Creator who is not bound by any laws of physics.

> **The earth was a formless wasteland, and darkness covered the abyss, while a mighty wind swept over the waters.**

Genesis 1:2.

Once again, and this will be seen to be a repetitive occurrence, Genesis provides an astonishingly accurate description of the earliest phases of Creation. It begins by saying that the Earth is formless. Generally, we pass right over that word without much thought, but here we should stop and consider its meaning in the context of the Big Bang model. It does not mean that the Earth was a fiery, molten ball of primordial elements—that will come much later. It means it was formless. It had no discernible shape it all. It was like waffles before all the ingredients have been mixed together and poured onto the waffle iron. There is no semblance of waffles in the flour, eggs, buttermilk, and sugar. I am known with our family as the master waffle maker. Waffles are a treat I regularly prepare at family gatherings. Figure 28 shows my waffles "without form."

Figure 28 Waffles without form

So what's the big deal? Remember where this story of Creation came from. It is an oral tradition handed down from generation to generation in ancient times before it was finally committed to written form. This description of the Earth before it had form, according to modern scientific knowledge, was provided by a bunch of Stone Age families passing down their stories. There are no mythical battles of gods or sexual activities as seen in many ancient creation myths. There is simply God, acting through His own power creating in an orderly, methodical process an unimaginably huge universe, with Earth as formless ingredients within it. Ponder for a moment how could a Stone Age storyteller conceive of the idea of a formless Earth without Divine inspiration? Everything he could see around him had always been there. Yet, he tells a story of an Earth without form, created and formed through an orderly, step-by-step process at God's Word. This is a thought that should be kept in mind as we progress through this narration of Creation seen "through the eyes of faith."

Next we come upon the word darkness—"darkness covered the abyss." Although my thesis throughout this book has been the consistency of the Biblical Creation narrative with modern scientific discoveries, we have to recognize that that is not the purpose of the Bible at all. We do not go to the Bible for scientific discovery. The Bible is a story of the relationship between God and man. That is the principal context of the darkness in this instance and, indeed, in most instances in the Bible. In the Bible, darkness is a representation of evil. When Judas takes the morsel of food from Jesus and leaves to betray him, St. John's Gospel notes that it was night with a heavy implication of evil.

> **So he took the morsel and left at once. And it was night.**

John 13:30.

Note, also, that when Judas leaves, he leaves Jesus Christ, the Son of God, the Second person of the Holy Trinity. He leaves the face of God and goes into the night, into evil. The interesting thing about darkness is that it is not a thing at all. You cannot turn on darkness. You cannot make it. All you can do is remove the light. That is the theological nature of evil. It is separation from God.

Figure 29 Judas enters into darkness

When we turn ourselves away from the face of God, abandoning His will for how life should be lived and substitute our own moral code, we enter into darkness. We separate ourselves from the Light.

In the creation narrative, God has not created darkness—symbolically evil. He has not yet created light and darkness is merely the absence of light. Darkness is not a thing in itself.

Finally, in this short verse in Genesis we read of a mighty wind over water.

> **While a mighty wind swept over the waters.**

Genesis 1:2.

At this point in creation, there is no water; indeed, there are no molecules at all. However, water is an apt metaphor for the primordial soup of proto-atoms as they progress toward formation of the building blocks of all matter.

And over this incubator of Creation is a mighty wind. In Hebrew the same word is used for wind, breath, and spirit. This is a lyrical description of God, in the Person of the Holy Spirit gently watching over this apparent chaos of Creation as it conforms to His Will. He is like a breeze, gentle as a breath moving the results of

His Word. Later, in the creation of man, we will see this same commingling of breath and Spirit as Adam receives His immortal soul.

But for now, we have reached the point in the Big Bang scientific model of creation—the point when, 300,000 years after the singularity obediently sprang into existence at God's Word, we approach the appearance of light.

> **[D]arkeness was on the face of the deep; and the Spirit of God was moving over the face of the waters.**
>
> **Then God said, "Let there be light," and there was light.**

Genesis 1:2-3.

At about 300,000 years ago, the temperature of the matter within the universe cooled to a (relatively speaking) much more tolerable 10,000° C—down from a temperature exceeding $10^{27°}$ C at the first instant after the Big Bang. At the cooler temperature, two things began to happen. First, the hot swarm of individual electrons, protons, and neutrons began to lose enough energy to start combining into atoms of hydrogen gas and helium gas. The first atoms of creation have formed.

The second event was that the cooling reduced the wavelength of electromagnetic energy into the spectrum of visible light, although not that there was anyone around to see it. It's just a little hard to breathe when the only thing around is helium and hydrogen and, at 10,000° C, it is too warm to really get comfortable. It will be a few billion years, until humans are around to enjoy the spectacle of

Figure 30 Interstellar clouds of gas

Creation. However, as these swarms of helium and hydrogen atoms continue to cool over the next billion years, they begin to play a very important role. They will become attracted to each other and begin to coalesce into huge clumps of gas in the cosmos, which will eventually collapse to form the first stars. Such clouds of gas are still around today, such as the one pictured here in Figure 30—the Carina Nebula (NGC3372) photographed by NASA's Hubble telescope.

Again, let us pause to review the words of God in Genesis.

> **Then God said, "Let there be light," and there was light.**

Genesis 1:3.

We see that in the literal sense of Scripture, the light has appeared but we also notice that the stars have not yet formed. Again, Genesis describes in astonishing accuracy the appearance of light before the formation of the Sun, Moon, and stars. These will come later in the Genesis account, just as they come later in the modern scientific Big Bang model. We must again ponder the question, without divine inspiration—how could Stone Age tellers of the lore, without any education in mathematics or anything but the most primitive tools, pass on to generation after generation such precise information that was well beyond any human experience? They had never experienced a day in their lives when the Sun, Moon, and stars were not arrayed in all their beauty in the skies above them. From their knowledge, these celestials must have always been there, just as modern scientists believed until Edwin Hubbell's startling discovery in 1929. They had no reason to believe there had ever been a beginning. This was confirmed by the previously mentioned 1959 survey.[113] The universe had simply always been there. Indeed, as late as the Twentieth Century, even such notable scientists as Albert Einstein considered the universe to be "fixed and eternal."[114]

The idea that God had inspired Paleolithic storytellers with information that was infinitely beyond their understanding, I consider to be a gift from God to scientific minds. They would not comprehend the nugget of truth that had been given to them for tens of thousands of years. It occurs to me that this idea is somewhat akin to the process we go through when setting up some on-line internet account or arrangement. We enter a user name and then a password. Then, we are asked to answer a couple of security questions such as the name of our first pet or the mascot of our high school. These questions are a particular security arrangement so that our identity could be verified at a later time with information that only we would know. It seems that God has done the same thing. He has placed in the Holy Scripture certain information that only He could know, so that in later ages we would make these discoveries and conclude that He is indeed, truly the Source.

Sun, Moon, and Stars

You may have noticed that the only elements formed thus far have been hydrogen and helium. While helium and hydrogen are interesting elements, they are not very useful stuff for the construction of a solar system, much less a planet like Earth capable of sustaining life. According to current models describing the formation of the cosmos, for the next 10 billion years, huge gaseous clouds continued to be compressed until their mass formed enough pressure and heat to initiate nuclear fusion reactions of the hydrogen atoms, the stuff of hydrogen bombs. These nuclear furnaces composed of compressed gases are what we see as stars and, of course, our Sun is one of these stars. One of the byproducts of these immense nuclear forces was the formation of all of the heavier elements that make up our world today. When the hydrogen of a star was consumed, the star collapsed upon itself generating temperatures of 100 million degrees or more. Finally, these collapsed stars exploded in spectacular supernovas spreading all these heavy elements throughout the universe where they recollected into the more solid bodies of planets, comets, and other celestial bodies.[115]

Figure 31 Formation of the Solar System

About 4.6 billion years ago, our solar system began this process. A huge cloud of gaseous material began to coalesce primarily into the Sun; 99.9 percent of the mass of our solar system is in the Sun.[116] Figure 31 is a NASA artist's conception of the formation of the solar system. Material that was left over began to clump together in swirls circling the Sun. As particles in these swirls coagulated under gravitational attraction they formed the planets, moons, asteroids, and all the other parts of our solar system. As their mass increased, they also captured more and more particles from within the solar system and, in addition, they could capture more material from objects traversing the solar system. In only 200 million years, the Earth was essentially formed, though in a molten state.[117] Capturing more material sounds like a rather benign term, but it was anything but benign. About 4.5 billion years ago a chunk of matter the size of Mars smashed into the Earth spewing into space a large amount of material. This material, recombined into a large rock that continues to orbit the Earth. It is familiar to us as the Moon. [118] Similar collisions occurred on other planets forming their moons.

It has only been since the deployment of the orbiting Hubble telescope that scientists have actually seen the formlessness of a system of planets surrounding a young star. In the Orion Nebula, so named because it is in the constellation Orion, there lies a huge region of star formation. This region is just like the star formation region that spawned the Sun and our solar system. Some of the stars are so young that what will someday become planets are formless clouds of gas surrounding the emerging star. The Hubble telescope has captured some magnificent photographs of these star and planet formation areas. The picture in Figure 32 shows the beginnings of the formation of a planet from the formation dust of a new star. It is known as a protoplanetary disk or, in NASA jargon, a proplyd.

Later, I will address some of the exquisite features of Creation and our place in the universe that makes Earth conducive to life. But as a preview, the formation of our Moon is an example. Had the event which caused the formation of the Moon occurred while life existed upon the Earth, or should another such event occur in the future, all life on Earth would become extinct. This Moon forming event occurred during the first 200 million years of the infant Earth's existence, yet, in the 4.5 billion years since, nothing of that magnitude has occurred. Certainly, Earth has been hit by smaller meteorites or even asteroids, with cataclysmic results such as the impact that doomed the dinosaurs 65 million years ago,[119] but nothing like the Moon forming event.

Let's get back to Genesis and see what it has to say about the creation of our solar system. The first thing we will notice is the sequence in Genesis does not match up with the scientific models in all cases. This is not really surprising because the Bible is not a science book or a

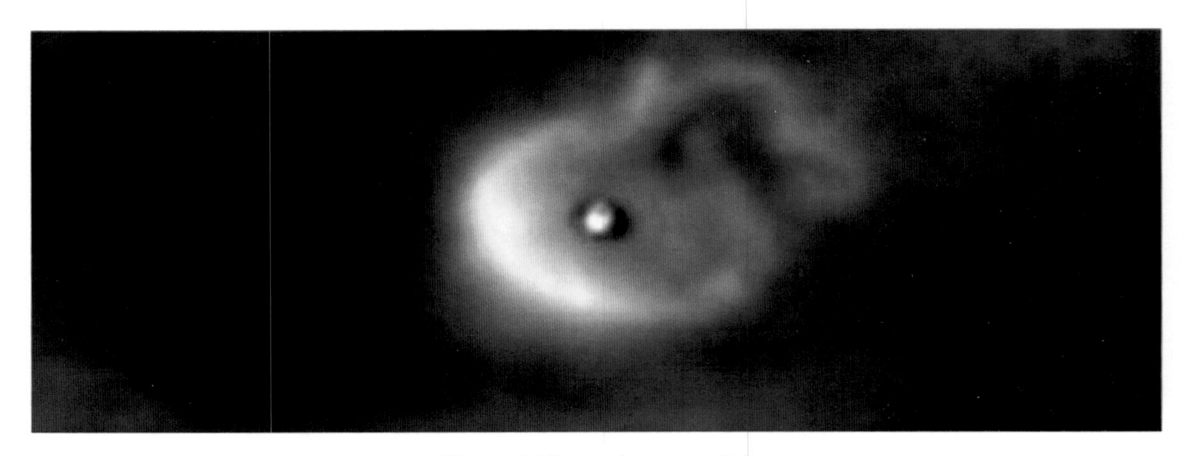

Figure 32 Protoplanetary disk

history book. It is a divinely inspired book describing God's relationship with mankind and His plan for salvation.

It is also a book written by many authors using different literary techniques. One of the effects of this is that it tells a story without necessarily abiding by rigorous time sequences. This is, also, not surprising given the Middle Eastern culture in which it was written. To this day, narratives and stories told by Middle Easterners do not always follow the sequential patterns we might expect in the West.

Admittedly, I have made much of the sequence of events in Genesis to this point and will again at appropriate times in later paragraphs. However, while the sequence is not particularly significant in this instance, the events that are captured are. Accordingly, I will describe the Creation events described by Genesis in the sequence laid out by the scientific models rather than in chapter and verse order of the text.

> **Then God said: "Let there be lights in the dome of the sky, to separate day from night. Let them mark the fixed times, the days and the years, and serve as luminaries in the dome of the sky, to shed light upon the earth." And so it happened: God made the two great lights, the greater one to govern the day, and the lesser one to govern the night; and he made the stars. God set them in the dome of the sky, to shed light upon the earth...**

Genesis 1:14-17.

Here we see the description of the sun, moon, and stars. There is not much discussion of how they were created; they were simply a creative act of God. We are now in the third day of Biblical Creation. As was noted before, Creation by God was a process, not an instantaneous response to one command. God accomplishes Creation of the universe in response to His commands or laws that he set into motion and continues to sustain. The amount of time involved is not significant in the Creation story because, whatever time it took, whether a day or a billion years, it was simply the processes at work over the amount of time required to achieve a particular desired state. That is all a day to God, who is not bound by our concepts of time. God existed before time began and will continue to exist after time comes to an end.

> **Then God said, "Let there be a dome in the middle of the waters, to separate one body of water from the other." And so it happened: God made the dome, and it separated the water above the dome from the water below it. God called the dome "the sky."**

Genesis 1:6-8.

Here we see again a very accurate, but unsurprising, description of the formation of Earth into the sparkling sapphire-like sphere we usually think of when we think of Earth, as it appears in Figure 33. If you stand in a flat area where you can see from horizon to horizon and look up, you see a perfect dome of sky, blue as water. No matter where you stand on Earth, the sky above forms a dome. As it appears to us, so it would have appeared to the keeper of the tribal lore to our earliest ancestors, and so he would have described it. The sky would have appeared to be a great dome of water just as the sea formed a great dome of water beneath the waves. Now, at last we have an Earth with a form, the form of a sphere, with a spherical dome of atmosphere above it.

However a truly smooth, spherical Earth would have been a problem for the eventual appearance of man, indeed for all land animals. A smooth Earth would have been completely covered with water to a depth of four kilometers, which is approximately 2.5 miles.[120] This problem was solved during the Moon forming event depicted in an artist's conception in Figure 34 when a Mars sized body struck the Earth and careened off leaving a huge gouge in the crust of the Earth. The material from this gouge and a much larger amount of material from the body that struck the Earth were captured by the Earth's gravitational field, eventually forming the Moon. The resulting gouge on the Earth left a huge basin into which all of the waters of the Earth could eventually drain. Once more, the resulting effect is succinctly described in Genesis.

Figure 33 Spherical blue Earth

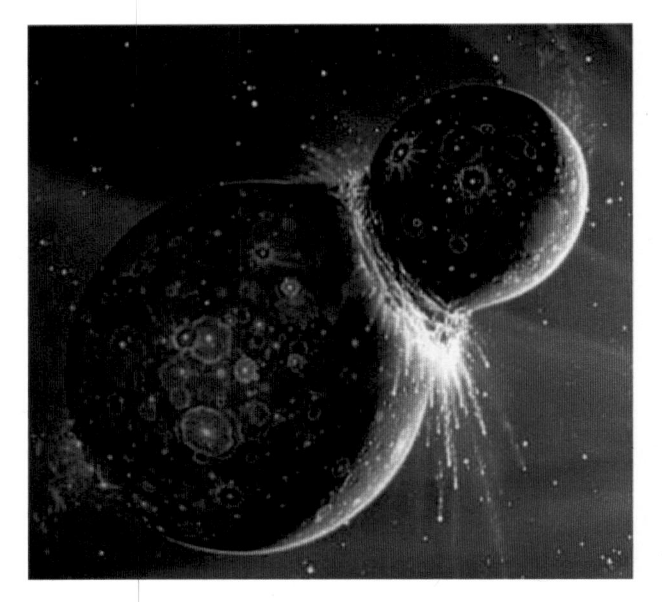

Figure 34 Moon forming event

Then God said, "Let the water under the sky be gathered into a single basin, so that the dry land may appear." And so it happened: the water under the sky was gathered into its basin, and the dry land appeared. God called the dry land "the earth," and the basin of the water he called "the sea."

Genesis 1:9-10.

Of course, this is not a precise scientific description, but it is pretty close for a Stone Age storyteller to pass to succeeding generations. The waters were indeed gathered into a basin so the dry land could appear. This event occurred, according to the most recent generally accepted model, approximately 4.5 billion years ago when the Earth was a mere 50 million years old.[121] As time passed, the Earth's tectonic plates moved across the surface of the Earth

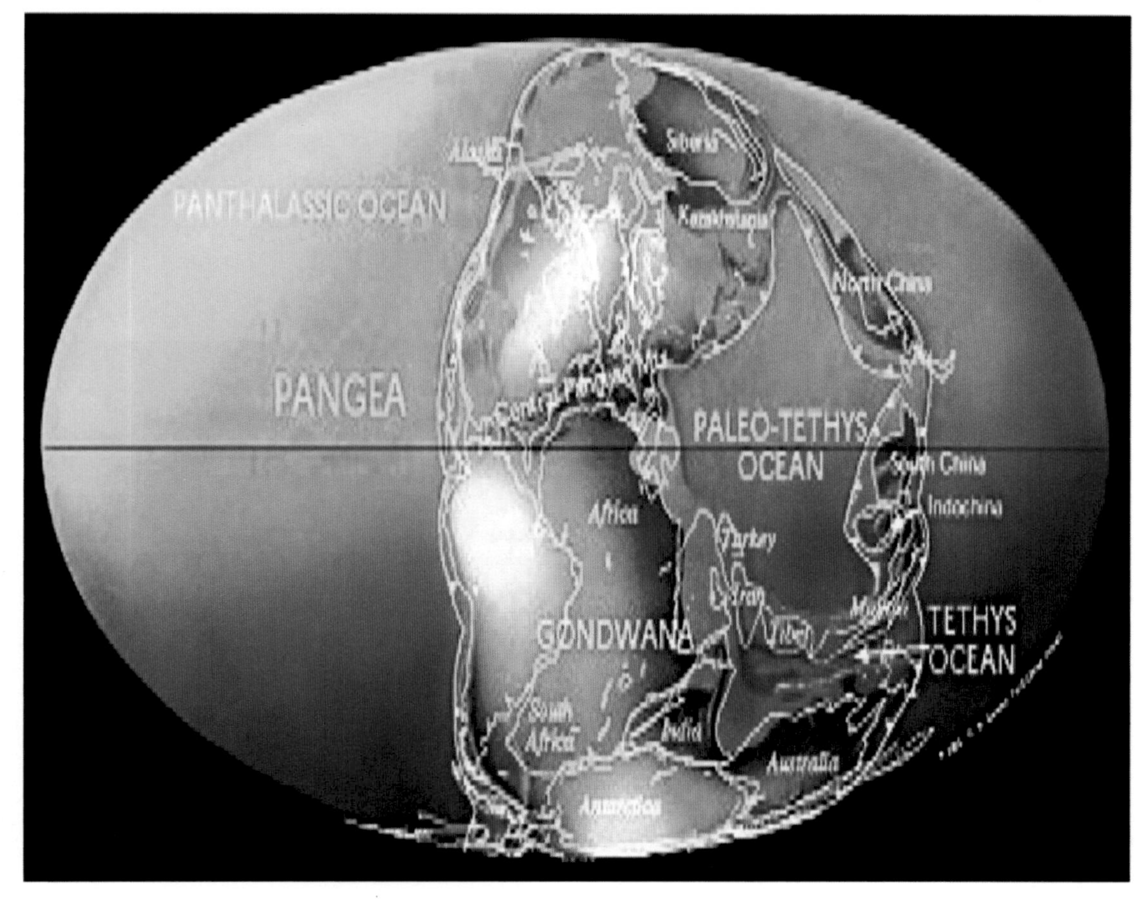

Figure 35 Pangaea supercontinent

separating this single land mass in subdivisions we call continents. However, these continents would occasionally come together again to form a large super continent and then split apart again. Over the last 4.5 billion years the continents have reformed into a single super continent at least four times. The last of these super continents occurred approximately 250 million years ago and was known as Pangaea. Figure 35 depicts this last super continent and its companion super oceanic basin. [122]

There was another effect of the Moon forming event that must be addressed. In addition to forming the Moon and separating the land mass from the basin for the oceans, the collision of the Moon-forming body was deemed to have been an off-center impact. As a consequence of this, the Earth received its initial spin. It was this initial spin which gave the Earth the familiar 24 hour rotation that brings us day and night. Our satellite and manned space expedition have given us breathtaking vistas of the Earth with a clearly discernible demarcation between night and day as seen in Figure 36. Yet again, this model of the early formation of the events of the Earth is described in Genesis.

> **God then separated the light from the darkness. God called the light "day," and the darkness he called "night."**

Genesis 1:4-5.

Looking closely at this initial spin and the beginning of day and night, we can see just how important this event was. Without the spin, the Earth would revolve around the Sun with one side always facing the Sun and one side always in night. This would have resulted in extreme climate differentials where the sunny side would have been extremely hot and the dark side would have been a frozen wasteland where all the water was solid ice. Only at the edges of the boundary between night and day would the ice melt only to be boiled away in the constant Sunlight. Such an Earth would have been extremely inhospitable for life. As we shall see later, life began on Earth in the sea as anaerobic bacteria. But had those seas been frozen on one side and boiled away on the other, it is doubtful that life would have formed in such an environment.

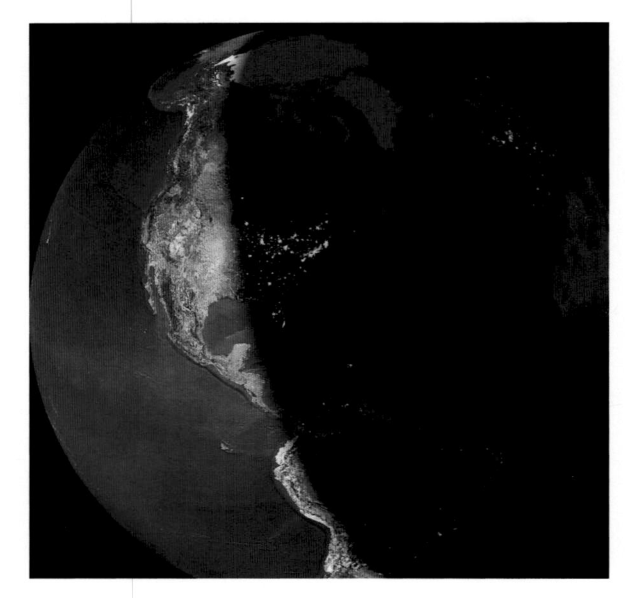

Figure 36 Day night demarcation

Let's get a little more specific by considering Mercury seen in the NASA photograph in Figure 37. For a long time, scientists thought that the day and year on Mercury were the same, so that Mercury kept the same side toward the Sun just as Earth's Moon keeps the same side toward Earth. More recent measurements show that this is not quite true. A year on Mercury is approximately 88 Earth days, i.e. it revolves around the Sun once every 88 days.

The length of a day on Mercury is approximately 59 Earth days. However, the effect is that the sunny side reaches temperatures of 800 degrees Fahrenheit and the dark side plunges to minus 279 degrees Fahrenheit. Because the Earth is more distant from the Sun, without the spin, the Earth's sunny side would have been somewhat cooler than Mercury, but the dark side would have

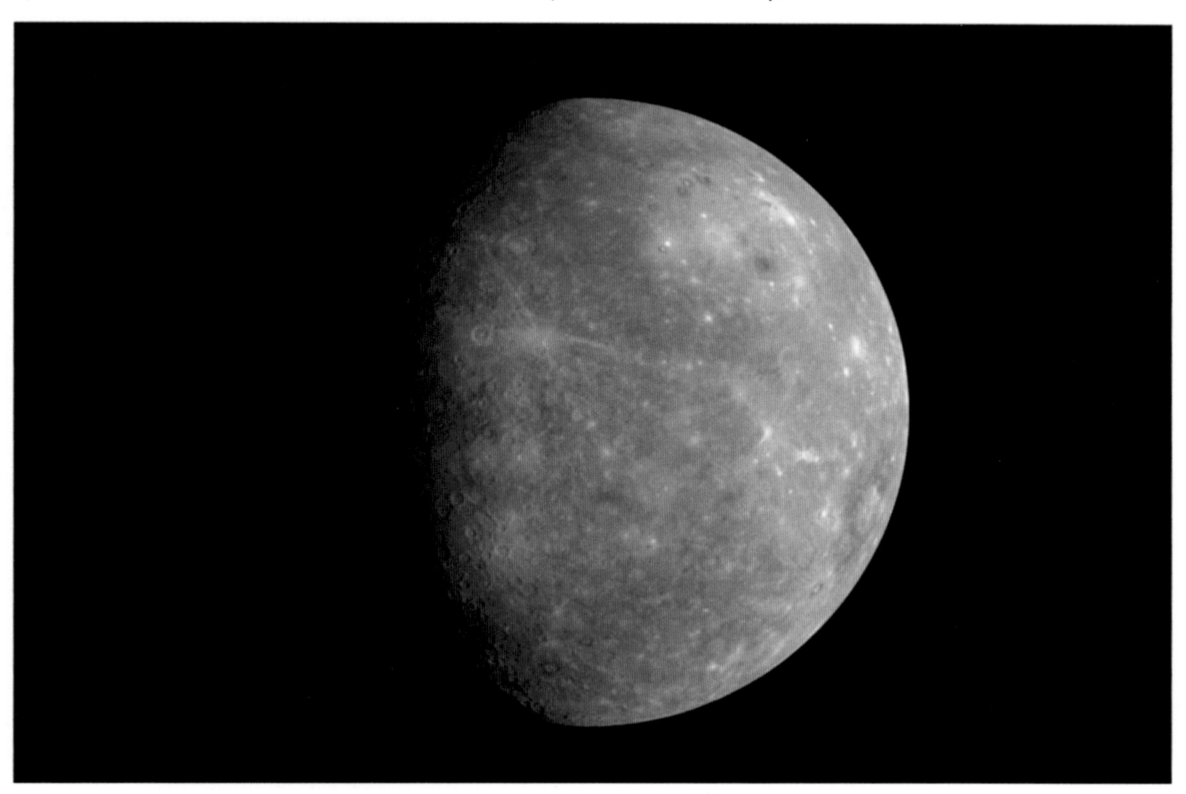

Figure 37 Mercury
A year on Mercury is but 88 Earth days;
yet a day is 59 Earth days.

been considerably colder.[123]

In the book of the Prophet Job, there is an additional short description of the hand of God at work in creation that gives a surprising description of the Earth's position in the universe.

> **He stretches out the North over empty space, and suspends the earth over nothing at all; He has marked out a circle on the surface of the deep as the boundary of light and darkness.**

Job 26:7, 10.

A footnote in the New American Bible explains the meaning of "the North" in this context:

> The North: used here as a synonym for the firmament, the heavens[124]

It is almost as if Job had been sitting on the Moon looking at the Earth rising over the horizon marveling at the wonder of God's Creation just as American astronauts would thousands of years later. Indeed, they took the photograph in Figure 38. There was the Earth with all its sapphire beauty, suspended in the heavens, closely matching the word picture created by Job.

We normally think of the descriptions of the Earth as a sphere as something that was not realized until the time of Columbus. Yet, here is a description that dates from sometime between the seventh and fifth centuries B.C.[125] It is a description that describes a spherical Earth suspended in space over nothing at all.

Figure 38 Earth suspended in the heavens, as seen from the moon

The "circle" was the Hebrew word for sphere.[126] The spherical Earth creates a circular horizon forming a boundary between light and darkness; light on the side facing the Sun, darkness on the side away from the Sun.[127]

We also find a description of a spherical Earth in the Book of Isaiah. Isaiah lived and did his work as a prophet of the Lord in the second half of the eighth century B.C.[128] Note that here, as elsewhere, biblical descriptions of the Earth are not flat, as scientific minds centuries later would erroneously conclude. The Earth, as described in the eighth century B.C., is expressly circular:

> **Have you not known?**
> **Have you not heard?**
> **Has it not been told you from the beginning?**
> **Have you not understood from the foundations of the earth? It is he who sits above the circle of the earth.**

Isaiah 40:21-22.

At this point, the universe has been created. As a result of The Big Bang, every particle of matter that will ever be created has been created; every quantum of energy that will ever be created has been created, although through nuclear forces, and the equivalence of mass and energy, they may change between each other. The stars, Sun, and solar system, including the Earth and Moon, have formed, although physical processes continue in all of them causing constant change and adaptation. Everything in the universe is prepared for the next great stage in Creation—the emergence of life.

However, before we begin our discussion of the emergence of life, we should pause to reflect on just how precisely everything has come together in a way that will support life. This miraculous chain of events, this degree of precision and timing, when looked at "through the eyes of faith," simply cannot be accidental or random.

Expansion of the Universe

As the universe began its expansion at the Big Bang, there is a critical rate in the range of possible rates of expansion that would correspond to our present rate of expansion. Had the rate of expansion one second after the Big Bang been smaller by even one part in 10^{17} the effect of gravity would have caused the entire universe to collapse upon itself and return to the singularity state, long before it reached its present size.[129] On the other hand, had the rate of expansion been greater than the critical rate, the universe would continue expanding forever and would gradually extinguish as their stars ran out of fuel.[130] It appears however, that the universe is expanding at very nearly the critical rate.[131]

Just Right Sun

It is a curious fact about the formation of stars that the larger (that is more massive) the faster the star will burn up all of its nuclear fuel and die out. Our Sun is thought by scientists to be at least a second or third generation star.[132] This means other stars have formed and burned out two or three times before the formation of our Sun.

In addition, the Sun is just the right size: not so massive that it would have burned up all of its fuel and died in a mere 100 million years or so, a period less than one tenth the age of the universe yet large enough to provide the energy needed for life. Our Sun is believed to have enough fuel to continue in operation for another 5 billion years.[133] These numbers are rather important. The most current estimate for the emergence of life on Earth is approximately 3.85 billion years ago.[134] If the Sun had only lasted 100 million years, it would have been long gone by the time we got here, except of course, we would never have arrived.

Good Timing

When we discussed the formation of the Moon, we talked about the impact of a Mars sized object striking the Earth and gouging out the Moon. Approximately 65 million years ago, the Earth was struck by an asteroid or comet that resulted in the extinction of more than half of the species on Earth including the dinosaurs. This asteroid or comet was believed to have been 110 to 180 miles in diameter. Consider the effect of this impact if it had been a Mars-sized object 4300 miles in diameter.[135] However, due to impeccable timing, the Moon formation event occurred long before any life appeared on the Earth.

Another result of the Earth's rotation is the Cariolis Effect. As the Earth rotates, anything moving in a straight line appears to curve to the right in the northern hemisphere and to the left in the southern hemisphere as the Earth moves beneath it.[136] The most obvious manifestation of the Cariolis Effect is the way your bath water swirls away as it goes down the drain. In the northern hemisphere it swirls clockwise and in the southern hemisphere it swirls counter-clock wise. This may not seem to be a particularly significant effect in the consideration of life on Earth, but the result is quite profound. The Cariolis Effect gives rise to our prevailing winds, in particular, the trade winds. It is this effect that causes low pressure to rotate one direction and high pressure areas to rotate in the opposite direction. This, of course, has a profound effect on our weather. The familiar spinning pattern of hurricanes is a direct result of the Cariolis Effect. Similarly, it has a major impact on our ocean currents and their weather effects.

Another characteristic we received from our off-center nudge was the tilt of the Earth's axis of rotation. It is this tilt that gives us our seasons of the year. While this may or may not be an essential perquisite for life, it certainly makes life a more enjoyable experience. Imagine a year with no springtime or no changing of the leaves. Certainly the Good Lord gave us beautiful things to enjoy in our lives.

Good Neighbors

About 65 million years ago, a meteor struck the Earth in the vicinity of the Yucatan peninsula in Mexico. The result was the extinction of 70 to 85 percent of the species alive at that time.[137] Fortunately for us, that included most of the dinosaurs. As a result, our ancestors did not have to compete with the likes of Tyrannosaurus Rex or packs of Velociraptors. The way was cleared for the emergence and dominance of smaller, smarter, more adaptable mammals, including Homo sapiens.

Perhaps, there is a tendency to feel sorry for the dinosaurs or think of them, with a degree of superiority, as a failed species. Before we begin to feel too superior, though, we should recall that the dinosaurs reigned supreme for 180 million years. Even some of our most ancient hominid species have only been around for a couple million years. And, vestiges of the dinosaur era remain. The goblin shark, for example, still roams the world's deepest waters, unchanged after 118 million years. Nevertheless, humanity can be glad the dinosaurs are gone.

Molten Core

The insides of the Earth are not well known and much of what is known is subject to controversy. The general model of the Earth's interior includes a solid inner core and a molten outer core. Because the outer core is fluid, it acts somewhat like an electric generator creating a magnetic field around the Earth.[138] One of the wonderful effects of the Earth's magnetic field for the continuation of life is that it tends to conduct much of the Sun's harmful cosmic radiation around and past the Earth. Just to show off how pretty as well as useful Earth's magnetic field is, those in the high northern or southern latitudes are treated to dazzling displays of the auroras depicted in Figure 39 as the deflected cosmic radiation interact with particles in the upper atmosphere.[139] But Earth's magnetic field is not just a pretty face.

It is essential for preventing our constant bombardment by solar radiation from simply ablating away our precious atmosphere. Without that molten core and resulting magnetosphere, Earth would be just as lifeless as any other planet.

However, I have often said that God has a sense of humor. He lays out little clues for His people to find as a reminder that he is here if we are willing to look "through the eyes of faith". Figure 40 is an artist's rendition of the magnetosphere at work created by NASA purely for scientific purposes and understanding. But, take another look "through the eyes of faith" to see if you can see the image of an angel protecting the Earth lovingly guarded at its heart. Is it an angel? Of course not, but "through the eyes of faith," it reminds us of the hand of God at work.

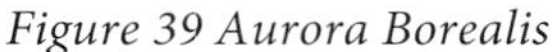

Figure 39 Aurora Borealis

Figure 40 Magnetic field deflecting solar radiation

Figure 41 Inner Planets

Location, Location, Location

Earth would have been uninhabitable if it been just a little closer to the Sun or just a little further away. Estimates vary but, the range is approximately five percent closer or 15 percent further away from the Sun.[140] Because of the Earth's elliptical orbit, its distance from the Sun varies—from about 91.4 million miles to 94.5 million miles.[141] Applying the habitable range estimate yields a habitable range of about 86.3 million miles to 108.7 million miles. Comparing these distances with Earth's closest neighbors, Venus and Mars, yields the results indicated in the table where the perihelion is the closest approach to the Sun and aphelion is the farthest extremity of the orbit around the Sun.

	Perihelion miles	Aphelion miles
Venus	66,782,000	67,693,000
Earth nominal	91,400,000	94,500,000
Earth habitable	86,300,000	108,700,000
Mars	128,400,000	154,900,000

Table 3 Habitable Regions

Table 3 reveals that the habitable region for complex life is a very narrow belt around the Sun. Earth, and Earth alone, resides in that belt in our solar system.

It is reasonable to ask whether either Mars or Venus would be habitable for complex life if either occupied Earth's position in the planetary order. One argument against that proposition is that neither Mars nor Venus has the magnetic field Earth has to protect would-be inhabitants from the effects of cosmic radiation. Therefore, Earth is the only planet in our solar system properly placed to support life.

The problem with this is that the Earth should not be where it is. If you look at the orbits of each planet, including the Asteroid Belt, each planet, with the lone exception of Earth, is approximately twice as distant from the Sun as the previous planet, see Table 4. Earth breaks the pattern.[143] We may wonder why. Was it a random event or intentional placement to sustain life? "Eyes of faith" will see the answer.

Mercury	Venus	Mars	Asteroids	Jupiter	Saturn	Uranus	Neptune
.38	.72	1.52	2-4	5.2	9.54	19.22	30.06

Table 4 Planetary distances from the Sun in Astronomical Units (distance between Earth and Sun)[142]

Shepherds

The amazing intricacy of the creation of the solar system has the Earth safely shepherded by the Sun and the tremendously more massive (than Earth) outer planets of Jupiter, Saturn, Uranus, and Neptune as depicted in Figure 42. Their gravitational attractions to massive bodies passing through the solar system slake them off protecting the Earth from the devastating consequences of large body impacts. In 1994, we had the good fortune to see just what such an impact would be like without having to experience it ourselves. In July of that year, a comet, designated Comet P/Shoemaker-Levy 9, that had broken up into at least 21 fragments,

Figure 42 Shepherds

some 2 kilometers in diameter, smashed into our good shepherd Jupiter.

From the vantage point of the Hubble telescope and the Galileo space probe, we were able to observe the impacts without getting too up close and personal. Such impacts on the Earth would have been catastrophic. Jupiter, however, is 1000 times the size of Earth, so it was able to absorb the impact. Just picturing these impacts on Earth, as seen in the accompanying NASA photograph in Figure 43, is enough to make one shudder.[144]

Figure 43 Comet fragments hit Jupiter

Atmosphere

The Earth's atmosphere is another prerequisite for life in more ways than merely the obvious medium for respiration. In fact, as we shall see later, the initial atmosphere of Earth was completely toxic to most things that live on Earth today. The atmosphere then was composed of hydrochloric acids, with precious little oxygen to breath.[145] Actually, our atmosphere is pretty thin as it is.

When we look up in the sky at a jet liner flying high above our heads, we tend to think the atmosphere is fairly thick. That jet liner may only be seven or eight miles high and the atmosphere extends up as high as 120 miles. Yet even that is miniscule compared to the size of the Earth. If the Earth were reduced to the size of your average classroom globe, the entire atmosphere would have about the thickness of a couple of coats of varnish.[146]

Thin as it may be, our atmosphere provides us with a remarkable degree of protection. It provides a greenhouse effect that keeps the Earth warm, which is an extremely good thing. Without it Earth would be in a perpetual ice age and there was be little opportunity for life to flourish.

Our atmosphere provides protection to varying degrees from cosmic radiation, ultraviolet rays and charged particles. One can imagine the damage these rays and particles would cause if unimpeded. Consider the serious effects they cause with skin cancer and the like, even with our protective atmosphere.

An additional, often overlooked, protection is the aerodynamic drag imposed on anything trying to pass through the atmosphere. Meteors generally burn themselves up due to the friction of the air long before they ever reach Earth's surface. Raindrops and hail are slowed to a soft pelting speed instead of smashing into us at hundreds of miles per hour. Consider the suicide victim who dies by jumping off a high bridge; that is the same effect precipitation would have on us without the aerodynamic drag.[147] These impediments in the atmosphere keep us alive.

And the point is…

Each of these factors makes Earth an extremely rare planet conducive to the formation and continued existence of life. So far as we know, there is no other place in our solar system that supports life. It is almost as if the Earth were designed specifically for the generation and preservation of life. When seen "through the eyes of faith," it was indeed specifically designed for that purpose. Even so, it is not a completely benign planet as the numerous extinctions through the ages would attest. All known life on Earth, including us, exists in a tiny band only about 12 miles thick. A thin sliver indeed when compared to the radius of the Earth or the expanse of the cosmos. As human beings, our habitable space is a mere fraction of even this thin sliver. On a volume basis, human beings cannot survive in 99.5 percent of that thin habitable space. We are quite confined on this perfectly designed planet we consider to be so hospitable.[148]

Let us pause for a moment to consider probabilities. If you flip a coin, there is a fifty percent chance it will be heads and a fifty percent chance it will be tails. No matter how many times you flip the coin that probability remains the same even if you just flipped ten consecutive heads. The probability is still fifty percent it will be heads. However, if your objective is to flip the coin twice and have two consecutive heads, the probability of that event is fifty percent times fifty percent (0.5 * 0.5) or twenty five percent. This is obvious if you look at two possible outcomes: two tails, two heads, first heads then tails, first tails then heads. There are four possible outcomes, only one of which satisfies the objective conditions. So, then, if our objective were to be to flip ten heads in a row, the probability of that would be 0.5 to the tenth power which is slightly more than seven percent.

Now, look at the probability of having each of the events we described as essential to complex, intelligent life occur as a random event.

- Expansion of the universe at slightly less than the critical rate
- Big sun, but not too big
- Timing of the Moon forming event
- Earth's rotation
- Tilted axis of rotation
- Extinction of creatures inimical to human survival such as dinosaurs
- Molten core
- Precise distance from the Sun
- Large outer planets protecting Earth from collisions
- Atmosphere

Each of these life essential characteristics has a probability of occurrence much less the fifty percent of the coin flipping discussion, yet each one is an essential element for a habitable planet, or at least habitable by creatures like us. Consider also, that this does not yet consider the probabilities involved in life springing up spontaneously. Those will be addressed later. Nevertheless, the physical conditions for life are very restrictive. It may be argued that with billions of galaxies each having billions of stars many of which may have planets, even a sequence events with very low, even infinitesimal probability, has a reasonable chance of occurring somewhere in the universe completely at random. Of course, the occurrence of life on another planet does not preclude another Divine act of God.

Those who argue against the possibility of Divine action in the creation of our planet and the life that thrives can simply point to evolution to say we simply evolved to live in the space available to us. Whatever truth there is to that argument, it still leaves open the possibility of God's role, and for one looking "through the eyes of faith," it is a certainty. There are simply many more places in our universe where life simply did not evolve to accommodate it. In fact, of course, we haven't found another one yet. There are possibilities on planets in other solar systems, but the conditions will need to be just right and the odds of that are pretty slim. Indeed, one may say astronomically low.

One of the more common arguments for the likelihood of finding extraterrestrial life is to invoke probabilities in conjunction with the huge numbers of galaxies stars and potential solar systems in the universe.

Stephen Hawking makes an argument for the almost mathematical certainty of the existence of extraterrestrial life. As one editorial explained,

> Hawking's logic on aliens is, for him, unusually simple. The universe, he points out, has 100 billion galaxies, each containing hundreds of millions of stars. In such a big place, Earth is unlikely to be the only planet where life has evolved.[149]

I would, given Stephen Hawking's stature, quite humbly submit that he has assumed the answer to his question, "Does life exist anywhere but on Earth?" To illustrate the flaw in his logic consider the following: Given that I have a legitimate, United States coin, I offer the question. What is the probability I flip the coin and that the coin will come up heads? The simple answer, of course, is 50 percent. However, that answer assumes that I will flip the coin. If I chose not to flip the coin, the correct answer is zero. Dr. Hawking assumes that the existence of life is simply a probabilistic event dependent only on finding the proper conditions. Even with a very low probability of occurrence, given enough trials, life will be found somewhere. Indeed, no matter how infinitesimally small the probability of an event, given an infinite number of trials, the event will occur. Consider flipping a quarter onto a hard, level surface. What is the probability it will end up on its edge? The probability of such an event occurring is infinitesimally small. However, given an infinite number of trials, that probability becomes a hundred percent.

Suppose now, that the emergence of life, rather than being a probabilistic event, is instead a predetermined choice by God. Either He chooses to create life on other worlds or He chooses not to. If He chooses to create life only on the Earth, contrary to Dr. Hawking's argument, it doesn't matter how many galaxies, stars, and planets there are; the probability of extraterrestrial life remains exactly zero.

At the present time there is not enough scientific evidence to support definitively either assumption. Indeed, should scientists eventually discover life on some other world, the question of assumptions will remain unresolved. It would still be theoretically possible for the secular assumption that the emergence of life is a random, probabilistic event to be true. It would be just as possible for God to have chosen to create life on more than one planet simply because it pleased Him to do so.

Looked at "through the eyes of faith," it does

not matter whether scientists discover life on another planet. That does not eliminate God's prerogative to create life wherever He pleases, on Earth alone or any number of other worlds.

Figure 44 Other Earths, other worlds

LIFE

Before embarking on a discussion of the creation of life, we should spend a little time addressing what, specifically, we are talking about. In saying, "What is life?" I do not mean what are the characteristics of life. These are fairly easy to define and explain. In general, living things ingest food, convert the food into energy, excrete waste products, grow, and reproduce. Webster's Dictionary defines life as: "an organismic state characterized by capacity for metabolism, growth, reaction to stimuli, and reproduction."[150] But, again, these are merely characteristics.

One reason life is difficult to define is that it is a process. However, we are able to define other processes without much difficulty. Take electricity, for example. Electricity is the directional movement of electrons among a series of atoms or molecules. The movement of these electrons creates a measurable effect that obeys specific defined natural laws. Similarly, chemical reactions can be defined, observed, measured, and predicted. Chemical reactions also obey specifically defined natural laws.

While we know that life involves chemical reactions such as the conversion of food into energy, and these chemical reactions follow the natural laws of other chemical reactions, life is not merely a chemical reaction. We cannot simply assemble all of the necessary chemicals in the proper proportions, add heat or electricity and obtain life. If that were so, we could resurrect a dead body simply by repeating the appropriate chemical process.

Bill Bryson recounted one such experiment in his book, *A Short History Of Nearly Everything*:

> In 1953, Stanley Miller, a graduate student at the University of Chicago, took two flasks—one containing a little water to represent a primeval ocean, the other holding a mixture of methane, ammonia,

> and hydrogen sulfide gases to represent Earth's early atmosphere—connected them with rubber tubes, and introduced some electrical sparks as a stand-in for lightning. After a few days, the water in the flasks had turned green and yellow in a hardy broth of amino acids, fatty acids, sugars, and other organic compounds.[151]

At the time there was a great deal of excitement about creation of life in a laboratory. In fact, it was no such thing. Although the acids created, particularly the amino acids are some of the basic materials for life, they are only materials. They are not life itself.

Indeed, it is proteins that are needed for life. To be sure, proteins are formed from amino acids brought together in a particular order. Each type of protein is different and requires a different structure of amino acids to form. It is estimated that human body has as many as a million types of proteins.[152] One of these proteins is named collagen. Collagen consists of 1055 amino acids arranged in precisely the right order. However, you don't make collagen. It makes itself as needed without anyone supplying the materials or an electric spark. It simply, spontaneously makes itself within a living body.[153] Outside a living body, it does not create itself and the odds of it springing up randomly are infinitesimally remote. For example, the probability of a mere 200 amino acid protein randomly and spontaneously appearing such that all of the amino acids occur in precisely the correct sequence is approximately 1 in 10^{260}. The number 10^{260} is greater than the number of all the atoms in the universe.[154] By comparison, the odds of winning the Florida Lotto jackpot played by picking six of fifty three numbers is approximately 1 in 23 million, that is 23 times 10^6. Florida Lotto is a much better bet.

However daunting these numbers may seem, they are not the whole story. The basic molecule of all living things is deoxyribonucleic acid, or DNA. As with most molecules, it is too small to be seen with the naked eye. The DNA molecule forms a helical pattern not unlike a long spring. If the human DNA molecule were to be uncoiled and stretched to its full length, it would be about six feet long. And it is this DNA molecule that makes each human being entirely unique from every other human being in the world or from every human being who has ever existed. Yet, this DNA molecule is comprised of only four protein types. One might ask how a molecule could produce the wide variety of unique human beings from an "alphabet" of only four letters, "proteins." Perhaps the ordinary personal computer makes a good analogy. Computers all over the world use a two digit alphabet—a one and a zero. It is the binary number system. Yet, for all of the millions of computers in the world, no two are identical, just as no two human beings are identical. However, they must be sufficiently alike or they would be some other species. Just how close must the DNA match? Consider the following:

> The chimpanzee and another ape, the bonobo, are humans' closest living relatives. These three species look alike in many ways, both in body and behavior. But for a clear understanding of how closely they are related, scientists compare their DNA, an essential molecule that's the instruction manual for building each species. Humans and chimps share a surprising 98.8 percent of their DNA.[155]

So what is life? "Through the eyes of faith," life is the unique Divine spark given to all living organisms. In the Nicene Creed, we profess, "We believe in the Holy Spirit, the Lord, the giver of life, who proceeds from the Father and the Son."[156] The Catholic Church teaches that human life begins at conception. From that moment onward, until natural death, life remains an inviolable right of every innocent human being.

> 2270 Human life must be respected and protected absolutely from the moment of conception. From the first moment of his existence, a human being must be recognized as having the rights of a person—among which is the inviolable right of every innocent being to life.[157]

At conception, the very first splitting of the fertilized egg into two cells, a process known as mitosis, all of the deoxyribonucleic acid, or much more simply, DNA, of the new living being are present. All of the chromosomes are present. The gender of the new being is determined by the presence of two X-chromosomes or one X and one Y-chromosome for the female or male genders, respectively. In other words, in human reproduction, they are little boys or little girls at that very first moment—the moment of conception. All of the DNA is present that will determine whether they will be tall like their father or short like their mother's side of the family. Whether they will have red hair or brown hair or be bald later in life is already determined at that point. Even their propensity to genetically transmitted diseases such as breast cancer or polycystic kidney disease (PKD) is present at conception. All that remains is for this new being to proceed with its natural development, which is an on-going, life-long process.

While science delves deeply into the processes of conception, it sees nothing but biological processes in the beginning of a new organism. Indeed, that is the realm of science. It sees nothing of the human spirit and nothing of the Divine miracle performed before their very eyes. But, "through the eyes of faith" we can see the hand of God at work in his new creation of every life—human, animal, or even plants—of every living thing.

The ancient Greeks described the human being using three words: *sarx*, *psuche*, *pneuma.* *Sarx* referred to the physical body with all its atoms, molecules, and physical components.[158] *Psuche* referred to the principle of physical life—that which makes us alive. To the Greek, everything that is alive, every human being, every animal, every tree has *psuche.*[159] *Pneuma* is the word for spirit. It is the thing that makes a man different from every living thing.[160] It is the Divine presence in every living person. The Hebrew words used in Genesis correspond exactly with the Greek concepts. *Tsimtsum* corresponds to created matter, in this case, the human body or *sarx. Nefesh* corresponds to the animal soul or *psuche.* And *neshema* corresponds to the human soul or *pneuma*[161]. We will address this further when we look at the creation of man. I, also, need to point out that while *sarx*, *psuche*, and *pneuma* may be a useful decomposition for analysis, the Church teaches an inseparable unity of the human person:

> 382 "Man, though made of body and soul, is a unity." The doctrine of the faith affirms that the spiritual and immortal soul is created immediately by God.[162]

The non-spiritual man may argue that life is merely a random event that, even though it has a very low probability of occurring, over billions of years it is bound to occur. This is the "million monkeys" argument. If a million monkeys randomly banged on the keys of a typewriter for an infinite length of time, they would eventually produce the works of Shakespeare. There are numerous problems with this assertion and its applicability to the random introduction of living organisms on the Earth, not the least of which is the monkey assertion itself. However, as an argument for spontaneous creation of life, it falls well short of the mark. As previously described, the probability involved in the production of the required proteins is orders of magnitude less likely than monkeys on typewriters producing the works of Shakespeare. However, given infinite time, any event no matter how low the probability of occurrence, will occur. However, the time frame for the emergence of life on Earth is not infinite. In fact, it is startlingly brief. From the time the Earth's surface became solid, about 3.9 billion years ago, until the first life forms appeared was only about 50 million years; less time than from the extinction of the dinosaurs until now.[163] It is also significant that in the intervening 3.85 billion years, no other life creating event occurred. It happened only once, and from that singular event, every living thing proceeded.[164]

The relatively rapid appearance of life on Earth, once conditions were at least minimally suitable, has given rise to rather exotic hypotheses that Earth was deliberately seeded with the materials necessary for life by extraterrestrial beings. Other than the extraterrestrial in question being God Himself, the argument does nothing to advance the understanding of the origins of life. The hypothesis merely moves the origin to some other planet, necessarily outside of our solar system and, therefore, many light years away.

It begs the question why any being with the capacity to travel through light years of space would do so for the purpose of sprinkling on a newly formed planet some very primitive dropping, which would eventually become life. For intelligent beings, it doesn't seem to be a smart approach. One would think they would start with some more advanced life forms. In fact, for the first two billion years of life on Earth, the only living organisms were bacteria.[165] That intelligent life intentionally seeded the Earth with the initial spark of life in the form of bacteria is extremely dubious. Perhaps the best to be said of these aliens is they certainly were patient. In any case, the argument requires a much greater degree of suspension of scientific methods than simply accepting Divine intervention. In addition, as we shall see quite shortly, the Biblically revealed Divine origin of life and its subsequent development closely tracks the scientific theories for formation of life based upon the fossil record; although, the converse is probably a more accurate statement.

Emergence of life

Now that the Earth, Sun, Moon, and stars have been created, God turns attention to the preparation of the Earth for the appearance of life and, in particular, intelligent life, that is us. As we left the status of the Earth, it had coalesced into a roughly spherical shape. The outer crust has formed while under the crust is molten rock and heavier elements. The Moon has been unceremoniously ripped from the Earth's crust and orbits the Earth. The Earth is constantly bombarded by space debris which brings such treasures as ice from passing comets and more of the heavier elements. At this point, there is no breathable atmosphere. Mostly, it consists of vapors of hydrochloric and sulfuric acids with virtually no oxygen.[166]

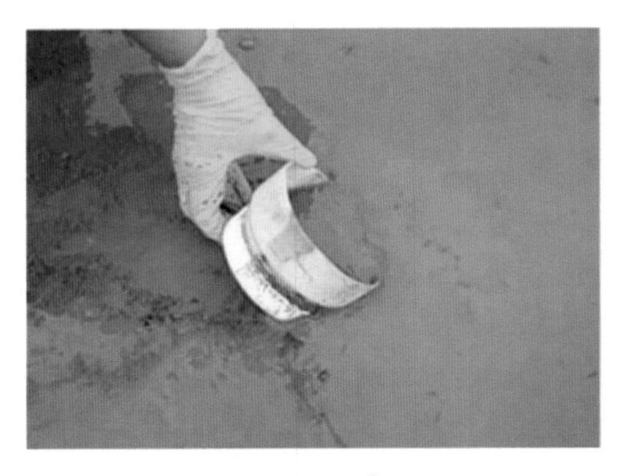

Figure 45 Cyanobacteria

> **Then God said, "Let the earth bring forth vegetation: every kind of plant that bears seed and every kind of fruit tree on earth that bears fruit with its seed in it." And so it happened.**
>
> **Genesis 1:11.**

The first living things that appeared on the Earth were anaerobic bacteria. These are bacteria that do not breathe oxygen. In fact, oxygen is poisonous to them. However, after about a billion years of bacterial life on the planet, one of these bacteria, cyanobacteria or blue-green algae depicted in Figure 45, began to absorb water molecules for their hydrogen and emit oxygen as a waste product.[167]

Typically, we think of living things as either plants or animals. Indeed, it has only been in the last few decades that scientists have further subdivided their definitions of living things.[168] Biological scientists, in their efforts to achieve greater precision, have defined at least five separate classifications of living things. These top level classifications are called kingdoms. I say, "at least," because there is always an on-going debate about the need to add additional kingdoms. In addition, there are some organisms, notably viruses which do not fit into any of the established classifications. However, on a macroscopic scale, most living things, at least those we can see with the naked eye, are either plants or animals. By this simplistic definition, the first of all living things to appear on the Earth were plants. In fact, the very process by which cyanobacteria converted the hydrogen in the water to its energy source, that is food, was photosynthesis; the first ever, as a matter of fact.[169] This, of course, is one of the identifying characteristics of plants. So, plants came first, according to science and according to Genesis.

About 450 million years ago, plants began to emerge from the seas and grow on the land. Additional organisms such as mites and bacteria emerged with the plants to turn the mulch of dead leaves and plants into recycled nutrients for the plants.[170] More complex animals will come later. Let us pause again for a moment to look at the time line from the emergence of plants. Plants were the earliest life on earth, beginning approximately 3.85 billion years ago.[171] For the first two billion years, that is, until about 1.8 billion years ago, the only living things on Earth were bacteria[172] and they were all anaerobic for the first billion years of that. Finally, at about 1.8 billion years ago a new type of organism called eukaryote appeared.[173] These are cells with a nucleus and internal membranes. After about another billion years, putting us at approximately 800 million years ago, these eukaryote cells began to be arranged in more complex multi-celled structures. This was a major development in the emergence of living things.[174] From this we see that the emergence of life was a long, slow-going process. Had it pleased God to do so, and as the omnipotent being we believe him to be it was certainly within His power to create the universe and the all living things just as they are today, in a single instant. It is evident from a reasoned view of our planet and our history, this was not the case. As we looked at the creation of the universe in Genesis, we saw a deliberate, step-by-step process. We are seeing again in Genesis this same stepwise process of the emergence of life. Once again, this process is astonishingly similar to the scientific evidence. In fact, it is far more similar to the scientific evidence than it is to anyone's actual life experience and particularly not within the life experience of Stone Age men who passed on the oral traditions of Creation over thousands of years.

> **Then God said, "Let the water teem with an abundance of living creatures, and on the earth let birds fly beneath the dome of the sky." And so it happened: God created the great sea monsters and all kinds of swimming creatures with which the water teems, and all kinds of winged birds. God saw how good it was, and God blessed them, saying, "Be fertile, multiply, and fill the water of the seas; and let the birds multiply on the earth."**

Genesis 1:20-22.

The next step in the process of the emergence of life on Earth overlaps the previous step. In the emergence of plant life, anaerobic bacteria appeared about 3.85 billion years ago. Then about 1.8 billion years ago the earliest eukaryotes (fully nucleated cells) appear. These are the foundation of all complex organisms for both plants and animals. Finally, about 450 million years ago, the first plants began to live on land.

As with the plants, the first animal life appears in the sea and stays there for a very long time. One reason was that the low levels of oxygen in the atmosphere did not provide a sufficient ozone layer to protect animals from the effects of cosmic radiation. The first somewhat complex, multi-cellular animal life was probably sponges. These first appear in the Cryogenian Period of the Neoproterozoic Era between 850 to 630 million years ago.

But, it was in the Cambrian Period of the Paleozoic Era between 542 to 488 million years ago that animal life truly exploded. Indeed, it is frequently referred to as the Cambrian explosion.

The Cambrian explosion occurred over a very short period, only 5 million year; hardly enough time for millions of years of evolution. Yet, the basic body type of every animal alive today developed within this short time span.[175] Such popular fossils as trilobites seen in Figure 46 emerged in this period about 540 million years ago.[176]

And, indeed, "the water teemed with an abundance of living creatures." The seas became the domain for all animal life throughout most of the Cambrian period, coming ashore toward the end of the Cambrian period about 400 million years ago. If not all, then nearly all creatures were non-vertebrates. There is some scientific debate about the existence of Cambrian vertebrates. This is probably a good point to address the nature of scientific debates as they relate to the history of creation of the universe and man as seen "through the eyes of faith." One of the goals of

Figure 46 Cambrian Period creatures

scientific investigation is to bring order to the understanding of nature. Scientists create numerous systems to categorize virtually every aspect of nature; for example the periodic table of elements. It must be understood that while these systems are orderly and systematic, they are, at the same time, arbitrary.

When additional subcategories are useful, or existing definitions are more useful if modified, scientists will quite easily adopt the new categories or definitions. I say "easily" with the understanding that it is not always, or even usually, without controversy. For example, in the last couple of years the status of Pluto as a planet has been hotly debated in the scientific communities because of changing definitions of categories of objects in space. Likewise, as we have already seen, the division of life into two categories, plants and animals, served the scientific community well for many decades. But, in the late 1960s, additional categories were added and even more are under debate. As we come to the emergence of man, the issue will become even more crucial as scientists apply their logic to define precisely what constitutes a human being. Indeed, the History Channel recently produced a documentary on just that debate. As a matter of seeing "through the eyes of faith," this should not be a problem. Scientists are free to define categories and propose new definitions to support their endeavors. But none of these systems of identification change the nature of life or the role of God in Creation. We need not become embroiled in these debates to appreciate the wonder of God's Creation and the on-going truth of His Word.

About 400 million years ago, creatures began to inhabit the land.[177] Initially, these were mostly small arthropods (animals with jointed, rigid exoskeletons such as millipedes), mites, and the first spiders. In addition animals called tetrapods appear on the land. Tetrapods are animals that walk on four legs and have feet ending in five fingers or toes.[178] Tetrapods are divided in scientific classifications into four main groups determined by the number and location of holes in their heads. Probably the best known of these creatures is the Dimetrodon shown in Figure 47. This was a large, sail backed reptile encountered by Pat Boone and James Mason in the 1959 movie adaptation of Jules Verne's *Journey to the Center of the Earth.* Although it looks very much like a dinosaur, technically it is not. Instead, it belongs to a subgroup of tetrapods that eventually evolved into mammals. However, there is a subgroup of tetrapods that are believed to have been the ancestors of dinosaurs.

As I began to notice the extraordinary similarities between the descriptions of Creation and the emergence of life on Earth in the Bible and developing scientific theories, I was somewhat puzzled by an anomaly in a developing pattern. The beginnings of the sea creatures and the birds on the fifth day did not seem to fit the pattern. We cannot and should not expect the descriptions of Creation in Genesis to be scientifically precise. These descriptions were recorded by men from the oral traditions handed down over countless generations. They are poetic, artistic, and literary; not scientific treatises. If a novelist, artist, scientist, and a person of faith were to describe the same sunset, the descriptions would vary wildly, yet each would have its elements of truth, and in fact, each would contribute to a more complete visualization of a sunset.

The novelist may elaborate on the mood created and the effects on the observers. The artist may describe the blends of color, contrasts of light, and reflections off the water. The scientist may describe wavelengths, coefficients of refraction, and the presence of water vapor in the atmosphere. And the person of faith might describe the wonders worked by the hand of God and the joy and beauty of living in His

Figure 47 Dimetrodon

Figure 48 Stone Age shaman

Creation.

All are correct in their own way, yet each is significantly different. In considering this concept in relation to the Biblical fifth day of Creation, it occurred to me that, in fact, the birds had been created on the fifth day just as Genesis described. But this Creation occurred in a way that would have been inconceivable to the Stone Age shaman seen in Figure 48 passing on the stories he had received from his predecessors. This inconceivable relationship was not even discovered by scientists until the 1970s and 1980s and is still a topic of debate. That discovery was that modern birds are the descendants of dinosaurs and, going somewhat further back, the descendants of the same subgroup of tetrapods (four-footed creatures) that first emerged in the Devonian Period about 400 million years ago. The birds, described in Genesis had their beginning on the Fifth Day along with the fish and other creatures of the sea. Those who passed these oral traditions and those that eventually wrote them down had no conception of a dinosaur. They had never even heard of such a thing, yet under the inspiration of the Holy Spirit, they captured something completely outside their knowledge and life experience. Unknowingly, they revealed an aspect of Creation that would not come to light for thousands of years. God seems to work that way, and indeed, He makes a point of it.

> **Rather, God chose the foolish of the world to shame the wise, and God chose the weak of the world to shame the strong, and God chose the lowly and despised of the world, those who count for nothing, to reduce to nothing those who are something, so that no human being might boast before God.**

1 Corinthians 1:27-29.

My hypothesis, about the birds mentioned in the Fifth Day, may not be entirely correct in light of Dr. Schroder's correlation of the birds of the Fifth Day, not as birds, but as winged animals such as dragonflies. These would fall within the definition as sea creatures in their larval stage as aquatic nymphs back in the section of the "Genesis Days" chapter. But, Dr. Schroeder continues with an analysis of the Hebrew in Genesis to identify the formation of dinosaurs on the Fifth Day.

> **God created the great sea monsters**

Genesis 1:21.

The Hebrew words that are translated as "sea monsters" are the words *gedolim taninim*. *Gedolim* means big. *Taninim* is the plural form of *taneen* which means animal. In particular, in Exodus when we read of Aaron's staff turning into a snake, the Hebrew word for snake is not *nahash* which is the word normally used for snake, but *taneen* which is a more general word for animal, and, in this case, a reptile. Therefore, the words in Genesis 1:21, *gedolim taninim,* would mean big reptile. When Moses was telling the Genesis story of Creation to the Israelites wandering in the wilderness, he would have used the words *gedolim taninim*, not dinosaurs.[179] The term dinosaur, meaning "terrible lizard," was not coined until 1841 by Sir Richard Owen.[180] Certainly, "big reptile" and "terrible lizard" are synonymous. All of this would put the formation of dinosaurs as a Fifth Day Creation event, beginning with their tetrapod ancestors 400 million years ago to their extinction 65 million years ago.

As we have progressed along in the description of the process of Creation and the emergence of life, both from a scientific viewpoint and "through the eyes of faith," it has become apparent that there is a direction to all of this. The universe has become more hospitable toward life and life has become more complex, more capable, and more intelligent. It is also true that the speed of development is accelerating. Creation began 13 billion years ago. Our solar system was formed about 4 billion years ago. Earth became habitable about 3.9 billion years ago and life appeared about 50 million years later. For about two billion years, the only living things were bacteria. More complex organisms appear 850 to 630 million years ago and at about 400 million years ago plants began to inhabit the land, followed about 50 million years later by animals including the first four footed animals.

Clearly, there is a direction to history. The processes leading to where we are today have not been haphazard and random. Life appeared on Earth once, and only once. Not just a new birth or newly evolved species, but no new foundation of life has appeared. The evolutionary process has been toward improvement and better creatures. Those that were eclipsed by their competitors died out and became extinct. Sometimes extinction came about because of inadequate adaptation, sometimes because of a cataclysmic event. In each case, by definition, the fittest survived and moved forward.

Seen "through the eyes of faith," this is evidence of the hand of God at work in His Creation. Thus far, the descriptions and advancements have been largely physical. Soon, development will move into intelligence and ultimately into the spiritual realm. As we examine this progression, we should keep in mind that history, indeed, has a direction and a purpose designed and executed by the mind of God. But, most interesting, and I cannot tell the significance, the pace of the movement of history is accelerating.

> **Then God said, "Let the earth bring forth all kinds of living creatures: cattle, creeping things, and wild animals of all kinds." And so it happened: God made all kinds of wild animals, all kinds of cattle, and all kinds of creeping things of the earth.**

Genesis 1:24-24.

Finally, in the last day of the Biblical Creation story, before God rested on the seventh day, He brought forth the animals of the Earth. Clearly, this process of creation overlaps the previous day when the first animals ventured out of the waters and began to inhabit the Earth. But, as we have said before, we do not expect the Biblical descriptions to strictly follow the scientific timelines and definitions defined by scientists. Yet, the process has been remarkably parallel and will continue to be so.

We now have a window of only about 450 million years for the development of all land dwelling creatures. That may seem like a long time, but compared to the history of the universe, it is a relatively short time. As we reach the emergence of man, that window will become significantly narrower. In fact, Bill Bryson, in *A Short History of Nearly Everything*, it is described as follows:

> Perhaps an even more effective way of grasping our extreme recentness as part of this 4.5 billion year-old picture is to stretch your arms to their fullest extent and imagine that width as the entire history of the Earth. On this scale, according to John McPhee in Basin and

> Range, the distance from the fingertips of one hand to the wrist of the other is Precambrian. All complex life is one hand, "and in a single stroke with a medium-grained nail file you could eradicate human history.181

That example only considered the history of the Earth from the time its crust solidified. If you go all the way back to the Big Bang, you need two more friends standing on either side fingertip to fingertip. Again we see that the process involved in the creation of complex, land-dwelling life overlaps with the previous "day of creation." Indeed, it has been a continuous process from the very beginning of life. The process, in the scientific world, is called evolution.

This name should not cause undue consternation among people of faith—though unfortunately it has. It is clear to those seeing "through the eyes of faith" the process began with God. It was by His Word that all things came into Creation, a Creation that scientists diligently search to describe and explain. It is certainly within the context of the Biblical description of Creation as a process occurring over a considerable period of time. That considerable period could certainly encompass millions, even billions, of years. The psalmist tells us, "a thousand years in Your eyes are merely a yesterday" (Psalm 90:4), to describe the eternal nature of God. Even the concept of one creature, including mankind, evolving over a period years into a new, more advanced creature that may be recognized scientifically as a new species, is not contrary to Church teaching. In 1950, His Holiness Pope Pius XII issued an encyclical entitled *Humani Generis* which addressed the issue:

> 36. For these reasons the Teaching Authority of the Church does not forbid that, in conformity with the present state of human sciences and sacred theology, research and discussions, on the part of men experienced in both fields, take place with regard to the doctrine of evolution, in as far as it inquires into the origin of the human body as coming from pre-existent and living matter -- for the Catholic faith obliges us to hold that souls are immediately created by God.182

We must keep in mind that the Theory of Evolution is a scientific model of the type described in the Introduction. It is useful for describing and categorizing observations and for making predictions about the nature of future outcomes. As we have seen in other examples, and continue to see quite frequently in the study of evolution, there is seldom unanimity of opinions and specific conclusions are subject to sometimes quite severe revision. It is also useful to remember that the classification of animals is also subject to the ebb and flow of scientific discourse brought on by new discoveries and re-interpretation of old discoveries.

A simple example of the evolutionary process is the development of the horse depicted in Figure 49. The evolution of the horse is described as a series of stages over a period of 60 million years, arriving at the modern horse about one million years ago. First, it must be noted that this series of stages is not discreet. Rather, it is one continuous process and the stages overlap each other. Scientists have classified fossils of the various horse ancestors as they met specifically defined criteria. Thus, at 40 million years ago, Eohippus did not suddenly disappear to be instantly replaced by Mesohippus. Rather, at 45 million years ago, Eohippus probably looked much more similar to Mesohippus than an Eohippus of 60 million years ago. It had simply not quite met the established definition of a Mesohippus, a definition that was specified long after Eohippus and Mesohippus had become part of the fossil record.

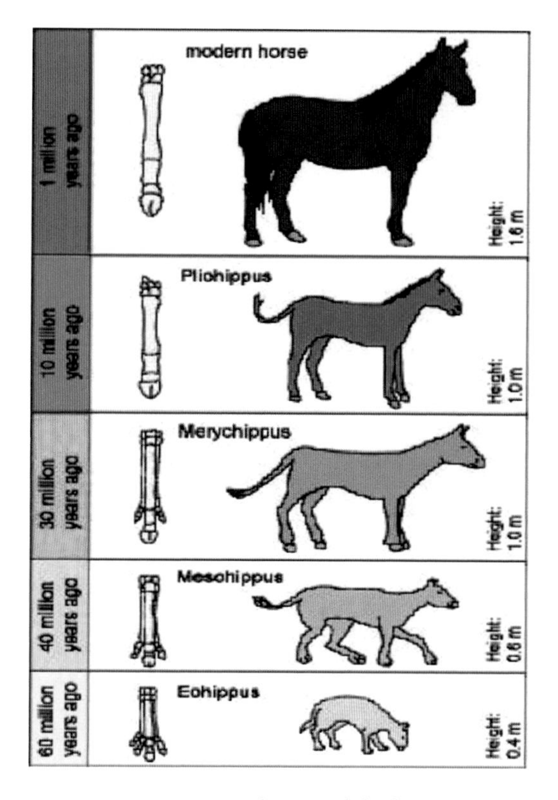

Figure 49 Evolution of the horse

One of the issues that has long faced the evolutionary scientific model is whether there is any evidence of one species becoming another species. While clearly, as the example of the horse above illustrates, it is not a matter of one species changing into another species. It is more of a matter of a species evolving characteristics that over a period of 10 to 20 million years, the characteristics of a species have become so different in size, skeletal arrangement, teeth, etc., that the classification system requires that the more modern animal be classified as a different species. This is keeping with the established scientific model, but does not break the relationship of a species to its progenitors. As we look at the ascent of man, this whole process becomes quite interesting because it occurs over a much shorter span of time. It involves lines that died out without tracing lineage to modern man and because there are so many overlapping strains of humanoid species.

A second issue facing the evolutionary model is the existence of sudden changes in very basic functions of the animal. For example, when animals first emerged from the sea, they had to learn to breathe air directly for their oxygen instead of filtering water through gills. Interestingly, when the early tetrapod ancestors of sea dwelling mammals, such as whales and porpoises, returned to the sea from whence they had come, they did not remember or relearn how to breathe in water. They simply return to the surface periodically for a nice breath of fresh air.

Nevertheless, the evolutionary model has been a useful one for scientists and it meets the basic criterion of being able to make predictions about the nature of future observations.

> **The LORD God formed man out of the clay of the ground and blew into his nostrils the breath of life, and so man became a living being.**

Genesis 2:7.

> **Then God said: "Let us make man in our image, after our likeness. Let them have dominion over the fish of the sea, the birds of the air, and the cattle, and over all the wild animals and all the creatures that crawl on the ground." God created man in his image; in the divine image he created him; male and female he created them. God blessed them, saying: "Be fertile and multiply; fill the earth and subdue it. Have dominion over the fish of the sea, the birds of the air, and all the living things that move on the earth."**

Genesis 1:26-28.

There are at least two distinct oral traditions that describe the creation of man in Genesis. They each give us their own perspective of the creation event. The idea that God used matter that had been created earlier is completely consistent with scientific evolutionary models of the emergence of man. Going back to the beginning of life on the planet, there was nothing but non-biological elements and molecules. They were in simple terms, "the clay of the ground."

When God created the spark of life in those primordial seas, the process was underway that would lead to all living things on Earth including the human species. It is true that scientists credit the rise of complex life, including humans, as survival of the fittest and random mutations that led to evolutionary advances. However, those looking "through the eyes of faith" can clearly see the hand of God guiding the history of the Earth, leading it to the point of creation of the human being, man with his full spiritual gifts created in the image of God. We will address that further, but first, let us examine the rise of man in the natural sense.

It is difficult to describe the rise of man, because new discoveries and re-evaluation of past discoveries have produced a constantly changing family tree of modern man. However, for our look at science "through the eyes of faith," the changes made to scientific models are part of the normal scientific process and are to be expected.

This does not affect the role of God in the creation of man. God's action remains constant even as the models change their understanding. With that said, we can look at the scientific model of the emergence of man using the latest data as of this writing, knowing it is changing even as we write.

Figure 50 represents only a snapshot of scientific analysis of the development of man—it covers a period of five million years, a relative nanosecond in the history of the Earth. The very upper left corner of the chart shows the emergence of Homo sapiens. Notice that the beginning and end of each species is not an abrupt line; there is an overlapping of species, as one evolves into the next in the line. Also, notice the blue arrow in the upper left corner of Figure 50. That indicates the approximate date of Mitochondrial Eve.

Eve appears at the very beginnings of Homo sapiens in the scientific models. She is, of course, as we know from Genesis, the mother of all living humans. This is true both in the scientific model and "through the eyes of faith." There are very few Homo sapiens fossils from the time frame of Eve in Africa, and many of those that do exist have Homo erectus or Homo neanderthalensis characteristics. That is exactly what one would expect in these periods of transition.

The timeline chart in Figure 50 shows the emergence of modern humans through a series of stages.[183] Some of these stages, such as Neanderthal man branch off without being true ancestors of modern man, although there are recent DNA analyses that recognize Neanderthal DNA in nearly all living humans.[184] This will be an important fact to consider later in the discussion of Noah's Great Flood. I believe that the crucial phrase in the evolution of man as described in Genesis is this statement:

> **The LORD God formed man out of the clay of the ground and blew into his nostrils the breath of life, and so man became a living being.**

Genesis 2:7.

Up until that point in human evolution, all of the humanoid ancestors of modern man were simply animals like the rest of the animal kingdom. Dr. Schroeder amplifies this point in *The Science of God*:

> Since the Bible defines a human as an animal with a *neshema*—the spiritual soul of humanity (Genesis 2:7)—there is no Biblical problem with human-looking creatures predating Adam. As Talmudic and ancient commentaries point out, they were animals with human shapes but lacking the *neshema* .[185]

They, like their human descendants and every other animal, shared the common attributes of life; the *psuche* described earlier.

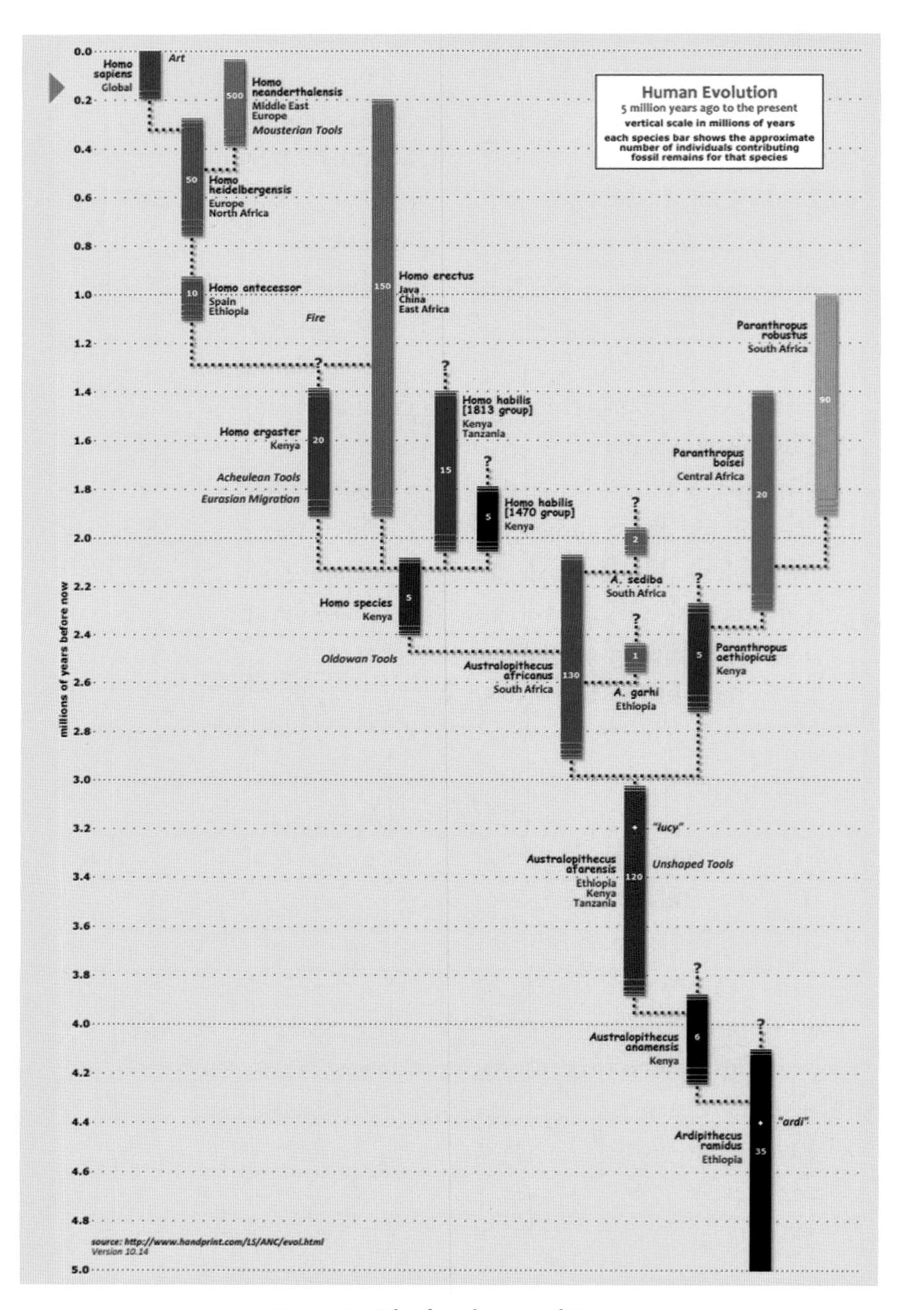

Figure 50 The family tree of Man

They were all living creatures. But, at the Biblical creation of man, God "blew into his nostrils the breath of life." Recall that in both the Hebrew and the Greek used in Biblical texts, the same word is used for both breath and Spirit. God blew His Spirit, the very image of God, into man and so man "became a living being." He became a living being, not in the sense of every other animal being alive, but in the sense of having a soul, eternal life that could only die through sin, by separating himself from God. This gift from God is what we mean in the Apostle's Creed when we say, "I believe in…life everlasting." The Catechism describes this unique gift and our awareness of it as follows:

> 33 The human person: with his openness to truth and beauty, his sense of moral goodness, his freedom and the voice of his conscience, with his longings for the infinite and for happiness, man questions himself about God's existence. In all this he discerns signs of his spiritual soul, the soul, the "seed of eternity we bear in ourselves, irreducible to the merely material", can have its origin only in God.[186]

Figure 51 Creation of Homo Spiritus

It also means that man received from God the inner law; an innate sense of right and wrong. These distinctly separate man from every other animal, no matter how intelligent it may be. However, we do not know exactly when this happened in the evolutionary process. It could have occurred in one of the scientific ancestors of modern man, or it could have happened to the creature known to scientists as Homo sapiens, that is modern man. One thing that is certain to those looking "through the eyes of faith" is that the man that God first blew His Spirit into was the man we call Adam. I prefer to call him, Homo Spiritus, man with the Spirit of God. Note also, that this was not an event that occurred through a process of evolution. There is no way to evolve into Homo Spiritus. We can only receive the Spirit of God through His Grace. At the perfect moment in time, God infused His Spirit into Adam. He was, from that moment on, unique from all other hominid creatures. I think Michele Giannetti's adaptation of Michael Angelo's famous work in the Sistine Chapel in Figure 51 captures the idea of God infusing His Spirit into an early hominid, separating him from all other creatures and becoming Homo spiritus. He would no longer see the world through the eyes of an animal. He would have to learn to cope with this new "image of God" and he would live in the presence of God.

> **That is why a man leaves his father and mother and clings to his wife, and the two of them become one body.**

Genesis 2:24.

> **He said in reply, "Have you not read that from the beginning the Creator 'made them male and female' and said, 'For this reason a man shall leave his father and mother and be joined to his wife, and the two shall become one flesh'? So they are no longer two, but one flesh. Therefore, what God has joined together, no human being must separate."**

Matthew 19:4-6.

One of the effects of man receiving the Spirit of God was a change in relationship with females. Typically in a group of animals, the most dominate male, the alpha male, claims sexual rights over all the females in a group. But, the relationship God creates with Adam and Eve, the pattern designed for us to follow for all time, is the unity of the body as a married couple. Thus, one man marries one woman for a lifetime of sacramental commitment blessed by the Church. The Catechism of the Catholic Church describes the vocation of marriage as follows:

> 1605 Holy Scripture affirms that man and woman were created for one another: "It is not good that the man should be alone." The woman, "flesh of his flesh," i.e., his counterpart, his equal, his nearest in all things, is given to him by God as a "helpmate"; she thus represents God from whom comes our help. "Therefore a man leaves his father and his mother and cleaves to his wife, and they become one flesh." The Lord himself shows that this signifies an unbreakable union of their two lives by recalling what the plan of the Creator had been "in the beginning": "So they are no longer two, but one flesh."[187]

From a spiritual view point, it is clear that the first man and woman to receive God's Spirit are the people the Bible refer to as Adam and Eve. In the past, I, like many people I suspect, considered the story of Adam and Eve to be merely a fictional Bible story used to instill a spiritual truth, but not necessarily a story about real people. However, science has made some rather astonishing discoveries that have concluded that all living men descended from a single male ancestor and all living women descended from a single female ancestor. These are known as Y-chromosomal Adam and Mitochondrial Eve.

Human cells contain two types of DNA: chromosomal DNA and mitochondrial DNA. Each human cell contains 23 chromosome pairs. In each pair, one chromosome is received from the father and one from the mother. In females, one X-chromosome is received from both mother and father. But, for males, the Y-chromosome alone comes from the father. The DNA in this chromosome can be traced from generation to generation.

Scientists have traced the male Y-chromosome DNA back to a single male who lived in Africa approximately 50,000 years ago. This single male was the ancestor of every male alive today. This does not mean that there were no other males alive at the time; indeed, there were many. However, all of the lines of descendants of all other males died out. Only the line of Y-chromosomal Adam exists today.

Before proceeding to a discussion of Mitochondrial Eve, I would like to return to my assertion that there were many other males of the same species alive at the same time as Y-chromosomal Adam. In addition to scientific evidence of many humanoid creatures during the evolution of the human species, we have an interesting Biblical clue of their existence. Immediately after God administers His punishment on Cain, Cain complains about the harshness of the punishment.

> **Since you have now banished me from the soil, and I must avoid your presence and become a restless wanderer on the earth, anyone may kill me at sight." Not so!" the LORD said to him. "If anyone kills Cain, Cain shall be avenged sevenfold." So the LORD put a mark on Cain, lest anyone should kill him at sight.**

Genesis 4:14-15.

At this point in the Bible, Adam and Eve have had only two children, Cain and Abel. A third son will be born to Adam and Eve about whom Eve made the following remark:

> **"God has granted me more offspring in place of Abel," she said, "because Cain slew him."**

Genesis 4:25.

So, who then is the "anyone" to whom both God and Cain refer? They can only refer to other humanoid creatures of the same species as Adam, Eve, and Cain but without the Spirit of God infused at their creation; as was done at the creation of Adam and the procreation of Cain. Our clue to the existence of other humanoid creatures of the same species is further reinforced in the succeeding two verses of Genesis:

> **Cain then left the LORD'S presence and settled in the land of Nod, east of Eden. Cain had relations with his wife, and she conceived and bore Enoch. Cain also became the founder of a city, which he named after his son Enoch.**

Genesis 4:16-17.

Here we see that Cain has been banished and moved away to the east of Eden where he took up residence with other humanoids and took a wife from among them and had at least one child, Enoch.

We can now return to the discussion of Y-chromosomal Adam and Mitochondrial Eve. The other type of DNA in the human cell is mitochondrial DNA. Women receive mitochondrial DNA only from their mothers. Scientists have been able to trace mitochondrial DNA back to a single woman who also lived in Africa, but she lived sometime between 150,000 and 200,000 years ago. In other words, every woman, indeed, every person, male or female alive today is a direct descendant of this single female—Mitochondrial Eve. Again, the Bible supplies us with this basic fact so recently discovered by our scientists.

> **The man called his wife Eve, because she became the mother of all the living.**

Genesis 3:20.

Consider this verse in Genesis recalling that it was probably not written until approximately the 6th century BC, even though it had undoubtedly been passed down orally from the time of Mitochondrial Eve. Without this verse from either written or oral tradition, how would anyone have known from their own life experience that every person alive today was a descendant of one single woman? Our life experience is quite the opposite. We look at all the people all over the world, seeing all their mothers, in the billions, and it seems impossible that everyone had a single common ancestor. Yet, contrary to our own life experience, modern science and the Bible agree, there really was an Eve as a real living person. Again, without Divine inspiration, how could our ancient ancestors have known?

At this point it appears that we have a problem if Y-chromosomal Adam and Mitochondrial Eve are indeed the Biblical Adam and Eve because they lived 100,000 years or more apart. In fact, numerous commentators on the scientific findings concerning Mitochondrial Eve and Y-chromosomal Adam think that this finding disproves the Biblical story of Adam and Eve. Actually, I think that the problem can be resolved in either of two ways. Either Adam lived at the same time as Mitochondrial Eve, between 150,000 and 200,000 years ago or Eve lived at the same time as Y-chromosomal Adam approximately 50,000 years ago. However, there are other considerations, especially much earlier migrations out of Africa than previously thought, therefore I will only address the case where Y-chromosomal Adam living at the same time as Mitochondrial Eve.

Since the Y-chromosomal Adam, and every other male offspring, received their Y-chromosomes from their father, then it follows that each preceding generation of fathers had the same Y-chromosomal DNA except for the first one. Although other males had differing Y-chromosomal DNA, one father in each generation of Y-chromosomal Adam's progenitors all the way back to 150,000 to 200,000 years ago had the Y-chromosomal DNA that we find in all human males today. We have very few fossil remains of that antiquity to examine (less than 150 over 5000 years old[188]).

Table 5 lists the Homo fossils that have been discovered in Africa near the time of Mitochondrial Eve 150,000 years ago. It would seem to be extremely difficult for any modern scientist to make the case that we have the very earliest Homo fossil with the Y-chromosomal marker. Do we really think we have the fossil remains of the father of the hominid referred to as Y-chromosomal Adam, or his grandfather? Further, is it reasonable, or at least

Common name	**Years ago (thousands)**	**Location**	**Homo Species similarities**
Heidleberg man	400-700	Germany	Heidelbergensis Erectus
Rhodesian man	200-125	Zambia	Heidelbergensis
Tautavel Man	400	France	Erectus
Petralona 1	250-500	Greece	Erectus
Atapuerca 5	300	Spain	Neanderthalensis
Omo 1 & 2	190	Ethiopia	Homo sapiens
Herto remains	160	Ethiopia	Homo sapiens
Jebel Irhoud 1-4	160	Morocco	Homo sapiens
Qafzeh 6, IX, VI,	90—100	Israel	Homo sapiens
Skhul V, IX	80—120	Israel	Homo sapiens
Klasies River Caves	75—125	South Africa	Homo sapiens

Table 5 Homo sapiens fossils

probabilistically likely, to think that for more than 100,000 years the line of every descendant of Mitochondrial Eve would die out except for the single female who would become the mate of Y-chromosomal Adam? It would seem much more likely that one single line of the offspring of Mitochondrial Eve and Y-chromosomal Adam would propagate over that 100,000 years, and all others died out. This time frame of 150,000 to 200,000 years ago would also be very near the very beginning of the Homo sapiens species depicted on the chart of Homo sapiens ancestry Figure 50. Therefore, Mitochondrial Eve and Y-chromosomal Adam's male ancestor could very well have been the Biblical Adam and Eve living at the same time. I will give science more time to catch up with the Bible.

Another reason to prefer the earlier Adam for the Biblical Adam and Eve who lived 150,000 to 200,000 years ago is that the earlier date will correspond to other developments in the rise of man which science has discovered and for which there are tantalizing clues in the Book of Genesis. These will be addressed in due course and the relevant connection will be identified.

> **The LORD God formed man out of the clay of the ground and blew into his nostrils the breath of life, and so man became a living being.**

Genesis 2:7.

At the creation of man, God breathed His Spirit into man, and man was made in the image of God. Adam received his immortal soul at that moment. In every succeeding generation, each person receives life and his immortal soul at the moment of conception.

> 366 The Church teaches that every spiritual soul is created immediately by God—it is not "produced" by the parents—and also that it is immortal: it does not perish when it separates from the body at death, and it will be reunited with the body at the final Resurrection.[189]
>
> 1711 Endowed with a spiritual soul, with intellect and with free will, the human person is from his very conception ordered to God and destined for eternal beatitude. He pursues his perfection in "seeking and loving what is true and good"[190]

God took a fully formed hominid creature, an animal, which He had created in a process that began with the creation of the universe, gave that creature His Spirit, his immortal soul, and that creature became the first human being. But, how did Eve get her immortal soul? Like Adam she was a fully formed hominid creature.

> **God created man in his image; in the divine image he created him; male and female he created them.**

Genesis 1:27.

I think the Bible gives a clue about how this occurred using the metaphor of Adam's rib.

> **The LORD God then built up into a woman the rib that he had taken**

from the man. When he brought her to the man, the man said: "This one, at last, is bone of my bones and flesh of my flesh; This one shall be called 'woman,' for out of 'her man' this one has been taken."

Genesis 2:22-23.

When God gave Eve her immortal soul, she became the second human being in existence. God had created them in His image and they had a bond that was unique in all of Creation. They were the only two human beings in existence in the entire world; the only two Homo spiritus. All other human beings would be their off-spring. They were separated from every other animal, animals that had been their companions.

I believe that man is the pinnacle of Creation, not because of any merit on his own part, but because of the great gift of the very image of God, his immortal soul. Man is unique in the animal kingdom. There are millions of species of bacteria and insects, thousands of species of fish, and hundreds of species of birds and mammals. Look at the animals in all of creation and there are other like species. Although there have been overlapping hominid species during the development of man, there exist today only one single species of man.

Of course, one of the major attributes of the human species that contributes to his uniqueness is his intelligence—his logic and creativity, his inborn natural law. These are the image of God apparent in His creation of man. If it were not for the action of God, why else of all the living things on Earth would only one single species evolve with the intelligence of man? There is nothing even close. No other creature invents or creates. There is no art or literature among the dolphins or chimpanzees.

Wesley Smith, in an article defending his book, "A Rat is a Pig is a Dog is a Boy: The Human Cost of the Animal Rights Movement," describes what he calls human exceptionalism:

> It is remarkable that our exceptional natures require defense. After all, what other species in the known history of life has transcended the tooth- and-claw world of naked natural selection to the point that, at least to some degree, we now control nature instead of being controlled by it? What other species builds civilizations, records history, creates art, makes music, thinks abstractly, envisions and fabricates machinery, improves life through science and engineering, or explores the deeper truths found in philosophy and religion? What other species rescues injured animals instead of ignoring or eating them? What other species has true freedom? Perhaps, most crucially, what other species can be held to moral account?[191]

Let us look for a moment at what this distinction means. In a pride of lions, and in many other species, when an alpha male is challenged by a younger male and is successfully driven from the pride, one of the

first things the new alpha male does is to kill all of the cubs of the defeated alpha male. All of the future cubs will be the offspring of the new champion. This is the natural order. It is no sin. The new alpha male has done nothing wrong.

Yet, for a human being to do something equivalent is understood to be utterly reprehensible. Why the different standard if man is nothing but another animal? It is because of the Spirit of God infused in humanity. He knows what is right and wrong even when he chooses to disobey. He may act contrary to that Spirit of God, but he knows, and he hides it. Even the most primitive man and all of our ancestors after receiving the image of God, the inner law, know it is wrong to kill an innocent person. It does not mean it does not happen; it means that man knows that it is wrong and will at least try to hide the deed.

Consider the first murder, when Cain killed his brother Abel. The first thing Cain did was lie about it.

> **Then the LORD asked Cain, "Where is your brother Abel?" He answered, "I do not know. Am I my brother's keeper?"**

Genesis 4:9.

Cain knew he had done something terribly wrong. He knew it without laws, without the

Figure 52 Lions battle for dominance

Ten Commandments, without any accusation. He instinctively knew it was wrong. This sense of right and wrong is present in no other animal.

Figure 53 Cain slays Abel

The Garden of Eden

Then the LORD God planted a garden in Eden, in the east, and he placed there the man whom he had formed. Out of the ground the LORD God made various trees grow that were delightful to look at and

good for food... A river rises in Eden to water the garden; beyond there it divides and becomes four branches...The name of the second river is the Gihon; it is the one that winds all through the land of Cush The name of the third river is the Tigris; it is the one that flows east of Asshur. The fourth river is the Euphrates.

Genesis 2:8-9, 10, 13-14.

Before we discuss the Garden of Eden, let's take a short geography quiz. Where are the following places: Cairo, Rome, Scotland? If you answered Egypt, Italy, and the British Isles, respectively, you are correct, of course. However, for the purposes of this discussion, these are not the correct answers. The correct answers are Illinois, Georgia, and a county in North Carolina. The point of this little quiz is that when people move to a new place where they have the opportunity to name things, they often name them after things in their place of origin. When settlers came from Scotland and settled in North Carolina, they named their county Scotland County.

The Garden of Eden is described as being near the Tigris and Euphrates Rivers. Most people assume this means an area around Iraq where these two rivers flow today. I think that the Tigris and Euphrates Rivers were named as they were because as humans migrated out of Africa, upon seeing these great rivers in modern day Iraq, they were reminded of some of the great rivers in Africa they had known or been told of in their family lore. The Genesis text provides some support for this hypothesis in its reference to the second of the four rivers which "winds all through the land of Cush." Cush is usually identified as being in Africa. When we later discuss migrations, we will see, in Figure 76, a purported location of Cush in eastern Africa near the southern end of the Red Sea.

Scientists think that early human ancestors, particularly the australopithecines and earlier hominid species lived in or among the trees. They came out of the trees and into the savanna regions on a more full time basis as they evolved into the early homo species.

The australopiths offer a superb example of mosaic evolution in which different features became humanlike at different times and at different rates. The unique combination of human and apelike morphologies makes the australopiths without close analogue in the modern world, and therefore extremely difficult to reconstruct with respect to function and behavior. Collectively, however, the available evidence strongly implies that these primitive hominids continued to make frequent use of arboreal habitats, even if they were fully committed bipeds on the ground. Some researchers have argued that the climbing abilities of *A. afarensis* may well have exceeded those of modern chimps, which routinely occupy trees in order to secure food and protective shelter.[192] While living among the trees, our early ancestors were truly living in a Garden of Eden. For food, they merely climbed a suitable tree and selected desirable shoots, nuts, and berries much the same as chimpanzees and gorillas do today. They did not have to work for their meals. No planting or cultivating of crops was required. This was just as described in the Bible of the days before the fall of Adam and Eve.

> **God also said: "See, I give you every seed-bearing plant all over the earth and every tree that has seed-bearing fruit on it to be your food."**

Genesis 1:29.

Once again, we see the sacred writers capturing an era of human life that had never been part their own life experiences. They had never experienced the herbivorous lifestyle, picking berries and nuts from the trees or eating tender shoots as they climbed among the trees or scurried about on the savannah as captured by Michele Giannetti's drawing in Figure 54. When they were writing, agriculture had been established for thousands of years. They hunted, but also tended domesticated animals for their food. Yet, these writers preserved the ancient stories handed down to them, sometimes in only a line or two in the Bible. It was only after leaving the trees, their Garden of Eden, that our human ancestors began to toil for their food. About 2.5 million years ago, about the time of the transition from australopithecines to the Homo species, our ancestors began to kill, butcher, and eat animal meat.[193]

Figure 54 Early hominids in Eden

Development of agriculture began sometime after the last Ice Age around 10,000 years ago. Ever since humans left the tree life of Africa, they have had to work for their food by the sweat of their brow, either as hunter—gatherers or by tilling the soil and raising crops. This change of food source is what the Bible describes after the fall of Adam and Eve when God cast them from the Garden of Eden.

> **To the man he said: "Because you listened to your wife and ate from the tree of which I had forbidden you to eat, cursed be the ground because of you! In toil shall you eat its yield all the days of your life. Thorns and thistles shall it bring forth to you, as you eat of the plants of the field. By the sweat of your face shall you get bread to eat."**

Genesis 3:17-19.

This change from an herbivorous to omnivorous diet was a momentous development of man depicted in Figure 55. Although this change occurred about 2.5 million years ago, it is nonetheless captured in the Bible. Whereas, before, God had given man the trees and fruit for food, later, in a specific action, God gave man the meat of every living creature for food.

> **Dread fear of you shall come upon all the animals of the earth and all the birds of the air, upon all the creatures that move about on the ground and all the fishes of the sea; into your power they are delivered. Every creature that is alive shall be yours to eat; I give them all to you as I did the green plants.**

Genesis 9:2-3.

This is an explicit statement in the oral traditions captured in Genesis recognizing this change of diet. Once again, it is something the Stone Age storytellers and those who wrote these oral traditions into the Bible could not have known from their personal experience. It was a fact, included in the Bible for the purpose of demonstrating to us the truth of the Word, and it was given to us through the inspiration of the Holy Spirit.

We have to continually remember that the Bible is not a history book nor is it a scientific treatise. Instead, it is something of a morality play in which we learn about God and our relationship with him and with our fellow man.

Figure 55 Early man, the omnivore

However, this morality play is set among real people and among events that actually occurred. They may not have occurred in exactly the same order as presented in the Bible and they may have occurred over a long period of time. This time may be compressed to facilitate the theological and moral message which is at its heart. I think the story of the Garden of Eden and the fall of man is a striking example of such a morality play. It is most unlikely that the sin of Adam involved eating the fruit of the wrong tree. As the Catechism of the Catholic Church states:

> 390 The account of the fall in Genesis uses figurative language, but affirms a primeval event, a deed that took place at the beginning of the history of man. Revelation gives us the certainty of faith that the whole of human history is marked by the original fault freely committed by our first parents.[194]

In sin, we turn away from God, walking away from His Presence. We prefer our own desires rather than trusting in Him. Whatever our first fully human ancestors did in rejecting God, it had immediate consequences as well as consequences that extended to us today.

When Adam and Eve committed the first sin, they did not have to be told. They instinctively knew that they had violated their relationship with God. As a result, they hid from Him and they made clothes to hide their nakedness.

> **Then the eyes of both of them were opened, and they realized that they were naked; so they sewed fig leaves together and made loincloths for themselves. When they heard the sound of the LORD God moving about in the garden at the breezy time of the day, the man and his wife hid themselves from the LORD God among the trees of the garden.**

Genesis 3:7-8.

Here again we see Genesis capturing an event in human development that no writer of the earliest Biblical texts could possibly have known. Consider your own lives. Our personal experience has always been that people wore clothes. Every generation grows up with people wearing clothes, except for primitive far away cultures. So, how could the Biblical writers have known that our ancient ancestors wore no clothes? For millions of years our humanoid ancestors wore no clothing. It was not until the time of Neanderthal man, 130,000 to 30,000 years ago that man began to wear clothes, specifically animal skins as depicted in Figure 56. It is certainly possible that early Stone Age storytellers told of the beginnings of clothes wearing.

I think it is also significant in the Genesis account that it is God Himself who first provides our ancestors with clothing made of leather, the skins of animals. At the time of the writing of the Bible most people wore clothes of

Figure 56 Early man wearing skins

cloth, not leather.

> **For the man and his wife the LORD God made leather garments, with which he clothed them.**

Genesis 3:21.

Another of the characteristics of our early hominid ancestors is bipedalism. Uniquely among all the creatures of the Earth including all creatures that have ever lived, humans walk fully erect. Fully erect walking probably did not begin until the transition from australopithecines to early homo species about 2.1 million years ago.

One of the consequences of bipedalism is that the pelvic bones have become thicker and stronger in humans than in non-bipedal animals such as the chimpanzee.

As a result of thickening, the birth canal among humans is significantly narrower than in other animals. This thickening and narrowing can be readily seen in the photograph of human pelvic bones (female top left, male top right) and a chimpanzee (below) in Figure 57. Compare these primate pelvic bones to a typical quadruped such as a cow, Figure 58. It doesn't take much imagination to realize that the birth process for human is much more difficult than for other animals. While I had read about this fact in scientific articles, it really did not have its full impact until I saw a video of an elephant giving birth. In this video it is clear that for a quadruped, the baby does not pass through the pelvic bones at all. This can clearly be seen at the moment of birth in Figure 59.

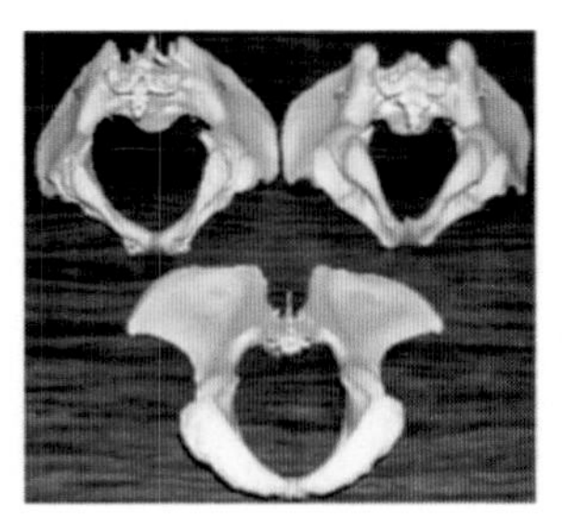

Figure 57 Primate pelvic bones

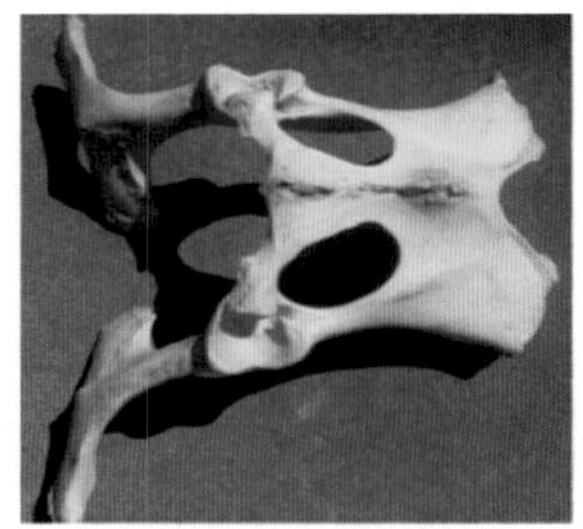

Figure 58 Bovine pelvic bone

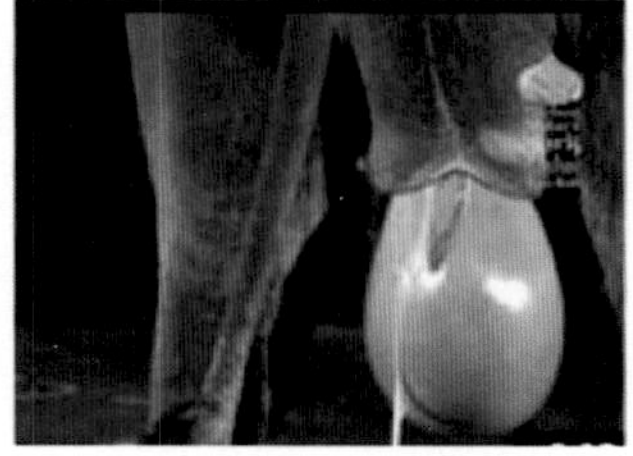

Figure 59 Elephant birth

So, one may ask, what does all this birth canal and pelvic bone thickness have to do with the Garden of Eden. Once again, the ancient storyteller has passed down events, in this case two million years old. He tells of the effect of man (actually woman) walking erect, resulting in greater pain in childbirth than for the other animals. The storyteller passing down this oral tradition associates this with the consequences of Original Sin.

> **To the woman he said: "I will intensify the pangs of your childbearing; in pain shall you bring forth children.**

Genesis 3:16.

Fire

For all the times Sacred Scripture refers to momentous events in man's development—being naked, then wearing clothes, being a herbivore, then becoming omnivorous, etc. It seemed strange to me that it appeared Genesis seemed not to mention the discovery of fire. Then I think I began to understand the way in which the Bible addresses this major developmental event.

In the early days of the evolution of the human species, man's ancestors lived among the other animals of the primordial forest. He competed with other animals for food and tried his best not to become food for some other predator. In fact, our hominid ancestors were fairly poorly equipped in that regard. Bill Bryson describes the early hominid vulnerability as follows:

> Even now as a species, we are almost preposterously vulnerable in the wild. Nearly every large animal you can care to name is stronger, faster, and toothier than us.[195]

Figure 60 Australopithecus afarensis

Indeed, our ancestors were frequently a tasty meal for large carnivores. Numerous fossils have been found with the teeth marks of ravenous predators such as leopards or even eagles. The ability of hominids to think and reason, superior to the prehistoric animals they encountered, was of little advantage in the event of an attack. Brains could not help them run faster or fight harder. In the wilderness, it seemed, our ancestors had few defenses.

Australopithecus afarensis pictured in Figure 60, the hominid whose remains have been dubbed Lucy lived approximately 3.2 million years ago. Compare Lucy to one of the predators believed to have lived in Africa during the same period. Though a fully grown adult, Lucy stood only three and a half feet tall. Whereas Agriotherium, a carnivorous bear, weighed a thousand pounds and was as large as any bear living today.[196] Figure 61 depicts a modern adult standing next to a modern Kodiak bear, which would be somewhat smaller than Agriotherium. Lucy would stand slightly taller than the man's waist.[197] Further, the fossil record finds hominid remains in the vicinity of fossils of these early, short-faced bears.

Figure 61 Kodiak bear

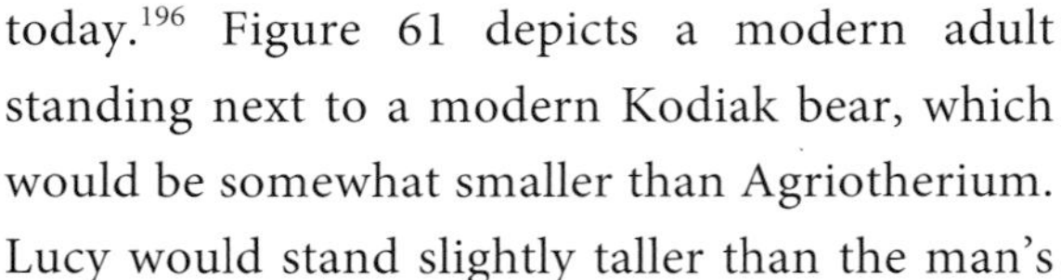

However, one of early man's great equalizers was the use of fire. There is rather unequivocal support among scientists for hominid control of fire 125,000 years ago. There is somewhat more disputed evidence that Homo erectus may have used fire as early as 400,000 years ago.

Figure 62 Control of fire

Some of the earliest claims of evidence for the use of fire go as far back as 1.7 million years.[198] Figure 62 depicts early man learning to control fire. One of the effects of early hominid use of fire is that the relationship with the other animals became radically changed. Using fire would undoubtedly cause a dread fear in other animals causing them to flee to a safe distance. This fear is described in the Bible as follows:

Dread fear of you shall come upon all the animals of the earth and all the birds of the air, upon all the creatures that move about on the ground and all the fishes of the sea; into your power they are delivered.
Genesis 9:2.

I think that one very strong clue to man's use of fire and the change in the relationship to other animals comes in the expulsion narrative from the Garden of Eden following man's Original Sin. This was a "you can never go home again" moment.

Never again would man enjoy the fruits of the Garden of Eden, restfully picking sustenance from the nearest bush or tree. He had left the trees and now, with the use of fire he would always be the outsider. Without in anyway negating the theological and moral importance of man's expulsion from the Garden of Eden, I think this was another real life event in the development of man that was used to describe the consequences of our actions. Thus, the Bible describes the angel wielding a fiery sword to keep man out of the garden. An ordinary sword would have sufficed since man had nothing but crude, stone tools at the time. But, I think the fiery sword is an indication of the connection with the use of fire by early man.

> **When he expelled the man, he settled him east of the Garden of Eden; and he stationed the cherubim and the fiery revolving sword, to guard the way to the tree of life.**

Genesis 3:24.

Death Came into the World

The Church teaches us that at conception, each human being receives his immortal soul directly from God, not from his parents. Since the soul is spiritual, it is completely undetectable by any human science, yet virtually every human being is aware of his spiritual self, however much he may try to suppress it.

> 366 The Church teaches that every spiritual soul is created immediately by God—it is not "produced" by the parents—and also that it is immortal: it does not perish when it separates from the body at death, and it will be reunited with the body at the final Resurrection.199

Since the soul is spiritual, it is also immortal to a point. It is immortal in that it lives forever, but it is subject to what Scripture sometimes refers to as the second death, that is, the eternal separation from God through our sin; our own desire to separate ourselves from God.

> **The victor will inherit these gifts, and I shall be his God, and he will be my son. But as for cowards, the unfaithful, the depraved, murderers, the unchaste, sorcerers, idol-worshipers, and deceivers of every sort, their lot is in the burning pool of fire and sulfur, which is the second death."**

Revelation 21:7-8.

One may ask about all the millions of human beings who lived and died before the time of Christ. What happened to their souls? Where did they go?

St. Peter gives an interesting insight in his

First Letter where he mentions those immortal souls who were dead in the body who heard our Lord preaching the Gospel to them. They were in a "place" awaiting the Resurrection of Our Lord.

> **For this is why the gospel was preached even to the dead that, though condemned in the flesh in human estimation, they might live in the spirit in the estimation of God.**

1 Peter 4:6.

I have always liked this picture in Figure 63, where we see Our Lord bringing the Gospel to the dead, because we also see King David, head bowed, greeting his Lord.

St. Paul tells us that through the sin of Adam, death came into the world.

> **For since death came through a human being, the resurrection of the dead came also through a human being. For just as in Adam all die, so too in Christ shall all be brought to life.**

1 Corinthians 15:21-22.

But, the scientific mind will immediately ask about all the other living things: the creatures, the dinosaurs, the pre-human hominids that lived, died, and some became fossils thousands, even millions of years before Adam or Christ. Certainly, death was in the world before Adam. Of course, "through the eyes of faith" we immediately see the distinction between death of the body, which has been an inevitable part of life from the creation of the very first microbe, and the "death" of the human spirit, which is immortal in that it exists forever. Spiritual death means to be eternally separated from God.

Figure 63 Our Lord preaching the Gospel to the dead

Our Church teaches that had Adam remained faithful and obedient to God, he would not have even suffered the death of the body. Through the effects of original sin, man joins all other creatures in physical death, but on the last day, his immortal spirit will be rejoined with an immortal, glorified, resurrected body.

> 400 The harmony in which they had found themselves, thanks to original justice, is now destroyed: the control of

> the soul's spiritual faculties over the body is shattered; the union of man and woman becomes subject to tensions, their relations henceforth marked by lust and domination. Harmony with creation is broken: visible creation has become alien and hostile to man. Because of man, creation is now subject "to its bondage to decay". Finally, the consequence explicitly foretold for this disobedience will come true: man will "return to the ground", for out of it he was taken. Death makes its entrance into human history.[200]

Thus we see all creatures suffer death of the body. However, because of his God-given immortal soul, man lives on after death as a spiritual being, until the final resurrection. Death of a human being at any time after conception is unique among living things. In addition to shutting down the functions of the body, there is a separation of the immortal soul from the mortal body. When a Christian goes to a funeral, he is confronted with the remains of the deceased, either in a casket or cremated ashes in an urn. But, the Christian must recognize that the person he once knew is no longer in that casket or urn. All the box contains are the earthly elements of the body. From ashes they came and to ashes they returned, as The Book of Wisdom describes:

> For haphazard were we born, and hereafter we shall be as though we had not been; because the breath in our nostrils is a smoke and reason is a spark at the beating of our hearts, and when this is quenched, our body will be ashes and our spirit will be poured abroad like unresisting air. (Wisdom 2:2-3).

The spirit separates from the body at death. It is the spirit that contains who we are. It is our intelligence, our memories, our experience, our personality, our very name. St. Paul tells of being called by God from his mother's womb.

> **(God), who from my mother's womb had set me apart and called me through his Grace.**

Galatians 1:15.

God told the prophet Jeremiah

> **Before I formed you in the womb I knew you, before you were born I dedicated you, a prophet to the nations I appointed you.**

Jeremiah 1:5.

And, we are told in the Book of Hebrews:

> **It is appointed that human beings die once, and after this the judgment**

Hebrews 9:27.

Finally, Our Lord told the Sadducees, who doubted the resurrection of the body:

> **That the dead will rise even Moses made known in the passage about the bush, when he called 'Lord' the God of Abraham, the God of Isaac, and the God of Jacob; and he is not God of the dead, but of the living, for to him all are alive.**

Luke 20:37-38.

Yes, we believe in a final resurrection of the body to a new, glorified body on the last day. But in the meantime, our spirit lives on after judgment, either in the presence of God or, by our own choice, eternally separated from Him.

Figure 64 Sebastien Bourdon's depiction of Moses before God and the burning bush

Purgatory

The idea that our immortal soul contains our "intelligence, our memories, our personality, our very name," has some important ramifications in regard to the change that takes place at death. Christians recognize that they are sinners. We are sinners, not by accident or by inadvertent slip-up; we are sinners because, by our own deliberate choice, we have elected to do what God has forbidden or neglected to do what God has commanded. Note that no lower animal species would ever do such a thing. Our sins are a product of our will. As Christians, we believe that, for the faithful, our sins have been forgiven and forever washed away by the Redeeming Blood of Christ shed for us on the cross. We further believe that Christ's Redeeming Sacrifice was effective for every human being who ever lived, is alive today, or will ever live. This one sacrifice accomplished the redemption of sins one time for all.

> 2100 The only perfect sacrifice is the one that Christ offered on the cross as a total offering to the Father's love and for our salvation. By uniting ourselves with his sacrifice we can make our lives a sacrifice to God.[201]

Although, our sins are forgiven, our sins have consequences. They affect other people leading them to sin, such as anger due to harm we have caused them. We are responsible for leading others to sin. In addition, sin, especially habitual sin enhances our own desire and inclination to sin. That inclination to sin is known by a nice, 25-cent word, concupiscence. The Catechism of the Catholic Church states:

> 978 We must still combat the movements of concupiscence that never cease leading us into evil[202]

Note that concupiscence is not, in itself a sin.

> 1264 Since concupiscence is left for us to wrestle with, it cannot harm those who do not consent but manfully resist it by the grace of Jesus Christ.[203]

At death, our soul separates from the body and goes before Christ for our particular judgment.

> 1022 Each man receives his eternal retribution in his immortal soul at the very moment of his death, in a particular judgment that refers his life to Christ: either entrance into the blessedness of heaven—through a purification or immediately—or immediate and everlasting damnation.[204]

However, this leads us to a conundrum at death. We know we are sinners during our lives. We can avail ourselves of the Sacrament of Reconciliation during our lives, we can seek forgiveness from the Church and from God. But concupiscence rages on, causing us to repeat sins over and over or go to one sin after another. We are incapable of living sin-free lives, even after forgiveness.

But, since our soul is the seat of our identity, our intelligence, and our will, it is also the seat of our concupiscence. Unless we are to continue our sinful ways in heaven, we must be purged of our concupiscence. As we enter into heaven, we must be purged or our pride, greed, envy, lust—all the desires of our will that lead us into sin. By purging us of concupiscence, we are no longer subject to temptation.

I have come to think that one of the major functions of Purgatory is nothing less than purging us of concupiscence.

Near Death Experience

I have previously stated that I firmly believe the teachings of the Church in every respect without reservation. That belief is based on the God-given authority of the Church and the specific guidance of the Holy Spirit to keep the Church inerrant and infallible in matters of faith and morals. In the case of the existence of the Spirit in human beings and the separation of the spirit at death, I have specific corroborating evidence, which I received first hand from my father.

As a young man, my father was involved in a serious accident. He was on a bicycle and had a collision with an automobile. He was taken to Tampa General Hospital for medical treatment. After extensive surgery, the attending physician concluded that my father's injuries were too severe and he could not be saved. A young doctor, who was assisting with the surgery, asked the attending physician if he could continue to try to save my father. To my good fortune, my father was successful and, during his convalescence, he met a young nurse in training who would eventually become his wife and my mother.

In my father's recounting of the event, he died during the surgery. He physically detached from his body and hovered over the operating table. Below him, he could see his body on the operating table, and he could hear what the doctors and nurses were saying. In particular, he heard the attending physician say that he could not be saved and the request of the young doctor to continue. The view he would have had would have looked very similar to the picture of the Tampa General Hospital Operating Room of that era in Figure 65 except, perhaps, he had been hovering a bit higher. There are several aspects of this event which lend it great credibility in my mind.

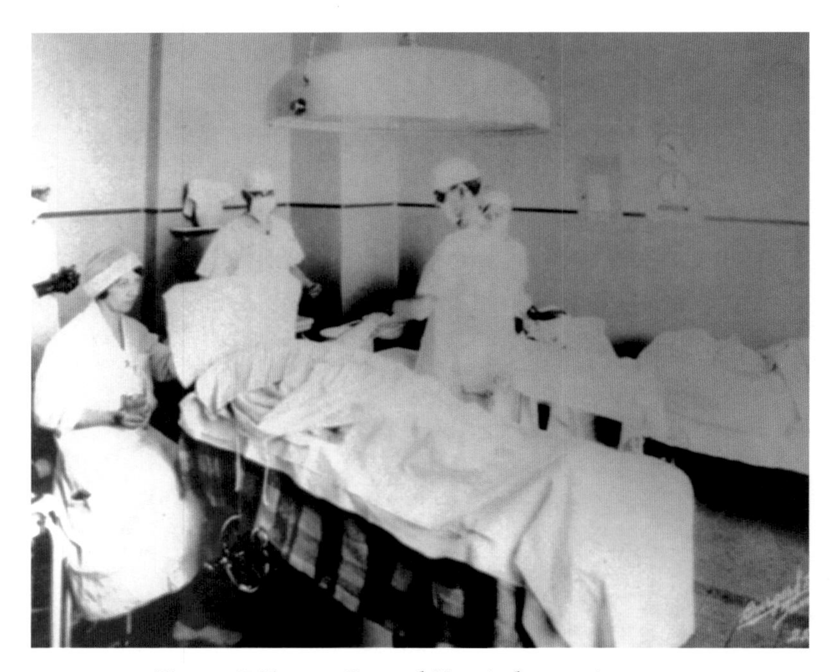

Figure 65 Tampa General Hospital operating room

First, my father was a very good and kind man, but he was not a man of faith. Although he was married in the Church and we attended services occasionally as a family, he eventually came to the conclusion that if there were a God, He was detached and impersonal. To my knowledge he never believed in the Christian God, and in particular, he did not believe in Christ. My hope and prayer is that at some point before his death, he did recognize and accept Jesus Christ.

Also, he saw no spiritual significance to his out of body, life after death, or near death experience. He did not see any tunnels of light, he did not encounter any deceased family members, and he did not encounter Christ in any form during this experience. In his mind, he had no reason or motivation to advance this story except that it represented his experience.

As for me, regardless of his lack of religious conviction, it was a confirmation of the existence of the human soul. It also corroborated the descriptions of post resurrection experiences described in the Bible, such as the ability to move freely in ways not available to living beings. His awareness of events that were occurring and his knowledge of things that happened or were said were very similar to teachings of the Church in regard to the Communion of saints. In particular, my father's experience seems to be similar to the ability of the saints of the Church Triumphant to be aware of our actions and our prayers, and to intercede for us in prayer before God.

The out of body experience of my father was literally a spiritual experience. His mind, his intellect, and his awareness were clearly separated from his body. Most interestingly, the physical elements of his senses were still with his body lying on the operating table. In particular, his eyes and ears were still with his body. Yet, he could hear and he could see. He was "seeing through the eyes of faith," yet, he did not acknowledge that. But, how else could he hover over the operating table and see his own body below him, or hear the conversation of the physicians? What other explanation, but his spirit separated from his body, could there possibly be? Few of us are granted the opportunity to experience our spiritual senses while separated from the body during this life. I don't know if my father ever realized what a Grace he had been given, but that blessing has flowed down to his children. Through his experience, we have recognized, in our own family, the human spirit that lives on in eternity, alive and in action, while separated from the body.

There have been many books written about near death experiences. Some tell of brightly lit tunnels or encounters with someone they recognized as Christ. Some tell of meeting with long dead friends or relatives. Many tell of sights and sounds while they were separated from their mortal bodies. Except for the separation from the body, my father experienced none of these other events. I can attest to none of these, except for the experience as told to me and other members of my family by my father.

Evil

One of the great philosophical questions concerning the existence of God is the question of evil. The question is sometimes framed as follows:

> Believers claim that God is omnipotent and that God is all good. However, since evil exists in the world, God cannot be omnipotent and all good. If God were omnipotent, He could exercise His almighty power and put a stop to evil. Since He does not do so, either He cannot and is, therefore not omnipotent; or He chooses not to, and He is therefore, not all good. Therefore, He is not God.[205]

Christian philosophers have wrestled with this question for centuries and have presented much better counter arguments than I can. However, I would like to add one original consideration to the argument as it pertains to the theme of this book that God's hand can be seen in the natural world. That consideration is this: evil is a relatively new invention brought into existence solely and uniquely by man.

Start with scripture. Throughout the Creation narrative, God repeatedly describes the result of His Creation as "good."

> **God saw how good the light was.**

Genesis 1:4.

> **God called the dry land "the earth," and the basin of the water he called "the sea." God saw how good it was.**

Genesis 1:10.

> **The earth brought forth every kind of plant that bears seed and every kind of fruit tree on earth that bears fruit with its seed in it. God saw how good it was.**

Genesis 1:12.

> **God made the two great lights, the greater one to govern the day, and the lesser one to govern the night; and he made the stars. God set them in the dome of the sky, to shed light upon the earth, to govern the day and the night, and to separate the light from the darkness. God saw how good it was.**

Genesis 1:16-18.

> **God created the great sea monsters and all kinds of swimming creatures with which the water teems, and all kinds of winged birds. God saw how good it was.**

Genesis 1:21.

> **God made all kinds of wild animals, all kinds of cattle, and all kinds of**

creeping things of the earth. God saw how good it was.

Genesis 1:24.

Indeed, it was good. There was no evil in the world at the moment of creation. If there is an overriding theme in the Book of Genesis, this is it. God's Creation existed for more than 14 billion years without a scintilla of evil. Often, we confuse compassion, especially toward the cute and cuddly, with a moral judgment about good and evil. When my son was a student at the University of Florida walking between classes one day, he saw a squirrel hopping around on the ground foraging for food. Suddenly, to the horror of fellow students passing by, a hawk swooped down, caught the squirrel, and began to shred it to pieces and eat it. The horror was that the cute, cuddly squirrel being torn apart by the mean, evil hawk.

Of course, it was no such thing. It was simply a real life demonstration of unfeeling nature in action. The squirrel was killed and eaten for food. There was nothing evil about it. Indeed, that is the fate of every living animal, from microscopic plankton to the largest shark, whale, tiger, or grizzly bear, including even humans. Every living animal will be eaten by another animal.

Maybe, as in the case of the squirrel and the hawk, it will be eaten by a carnivore higher up the food chain. Even the great white shark will eventually be injured and die to be eaten by fish, crabs, and worms as it settles to the bottom of the sea. The mighty lion hunting on the savannah suffering a broken jaw from a wildebeest, would-be prey, will weaken to the point it can no longer defend itself and be eaten by scavenger hyenas and vultures. There is no evil there.

But, man is different. Given the Spirit of God and the innate knowledge of the natural law, the difference between right and wrong, good and evil, man alone has the reason to make moral choices. When his moral choices conform to God's moral law, it is good. When man disregards God's moral law and acts contrary to it, we judge his actions to be evil. Thus, evil came into the world by an act of man against the moral dictates of God. This is precisely the Biblical story of the fall of Adam and Eve. Having first received the Spirit of God, their first rejection of God's moral law was what the Church calls Original Sin. We have continued down that path ever since. The only way for God to preclude man turning to evil would have been not to create man in the first place or create him as simply one more of the animals reacting to stimuli and instinct with no moral compass, no Spirit of God. Without his free will and the Spirit of God, man is nothing more than a clever primate and no matter how depraved we may judge his actions, there would be no such thing as evil, no rejection of God; because man would not be aware of the existence of God any more than the hawk or hyena.

ICE AGES

Typically, when we look at the Bible, we don't think much about the Ice Ages the Earth has endured. When we do think about Ice Ages in conjunction with the Bible, we find some rather profound implications.

Over the last 450,000 years or so, there have been four Ice Ages and a few "Little Ice Ages." Ice Ages produce a number of very significant effects upon the Earth, in addition to just making it cold. Let's start by looking at the ice core data. By drilling into deep ice, scientists are able to extract a core of ice. The deeper the ice, the older the time period it represents. By studying the lines on the ice, scientists can tell many things, just as much can be learned by studying tree rings. Additionally, by sampling bubbles within the ice, scientists can determine the relative amounts of various atmospheric gases captured in the bubbles in the ice. It is somewhat like a small time capsule preserved for us to study. For some reason, all of the charts make you read right to left, probably because you are looking backward in time. One thing you will notice is that it doesn't take a big change in our environment. For example, as one can see in Figure 66, the last Ice Age which reached its lowest temperature of about ten degrees Celsius lower than today, occurred about 22,000 years ago (BP—before present on the chart legend). It resulted in mile thick ice over New York and formed the basins of the Great Lakes only to fill them when the temperature warmed and the glaciers melted. We would probably consider both of those events to be pretty significant should they occur again, or perhaps I should say, when they occur again.

Indeed, looking at the chart, one could conclude that Ice Ages between relatively short periods of global warming are regular, cyclical events, and we are overdue for our next dramatic drop in temperature and ensuing Ice Age.

up in the glacier ice. This causes increasing aridity in the climate and it causes the ocean levels to drop. During the nadir of the last Ice Age, the depth of the oceans dropped by 400 feet. Conversely, when the Ice Age reaches its coldest and the temperatures turn around and

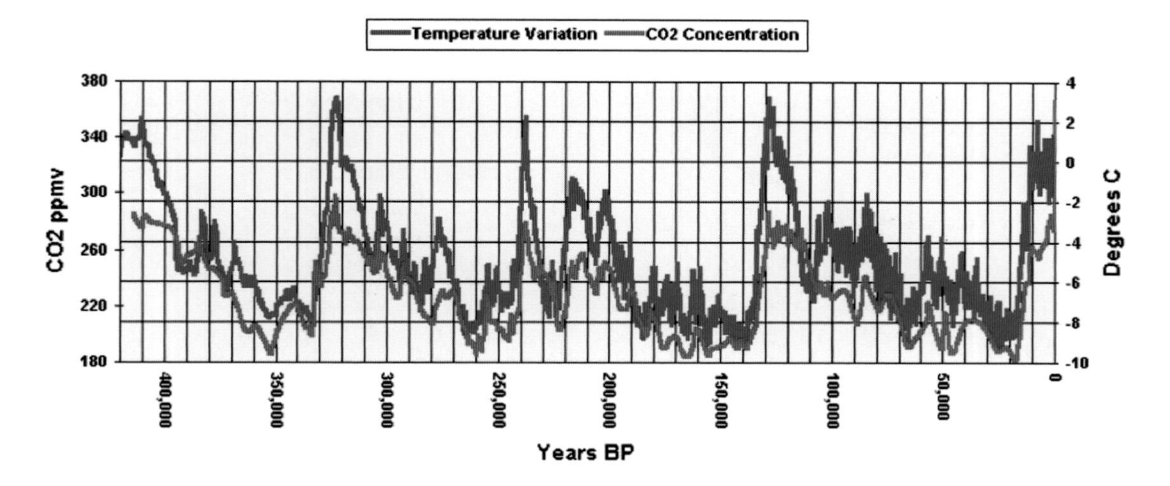

Figure 66 Ice Age data

When you look at the slope of the temperature lines on the chart, it also becomes apparent that when we enter an Ice Age or come out of one, the temperature drops or rises rather precipitously on a geological time basis.

When the temperature drops a few degrees, the snow that falls on glaciers never fully melts during the warm seasons of the year. This causes the snow to build up year after year making the glaciers grow. The glaciers continue to get thicker as more and more water is locked

begin to rise, the glaciers start to melt, releasing their captive water, and the ocean levels begin to rise as shown in Figure 67.

If you look at the history of agriculture, you will notice that the earliest evidence of cultivation is about 10,000 years ago. By that time, the period of global warming had been ongoing for about 12,000 years. This made a climate conducive to growing crops. Human innovation caught up with the changed climate, and civilization as we know it could begin.

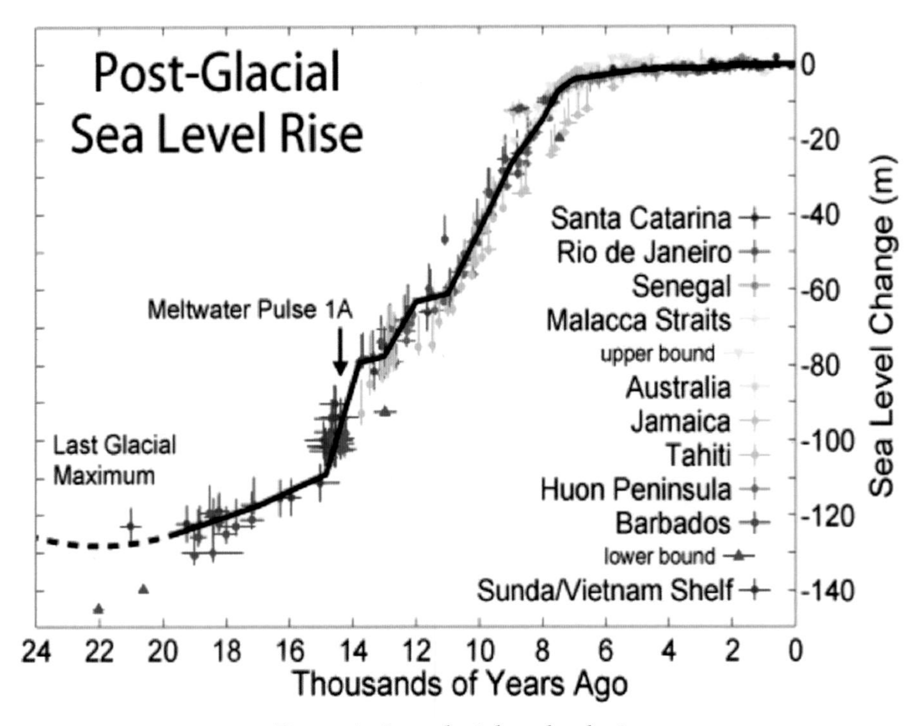

Figure 67 Post-glacial sea levels rise

By this time, you may be wondering why we are talking about Ice Ages in a book devoted to relating our faith to modern scientific discoveries. As we proceed, we will see numerous Biblical inferences to Ice Age effects. One point we must also be careful of is that there is nothing to indicate which particular Ice Age is exerting the influence. My general assumption is that we are referring to the Ice Age that reached its minimum temperature approximately 65,000 to 18,000 years ago. However, in some cases, it is possible that we are actually referring to an earlier Ice Age. Therefore, we should not be surprised when we think that some Biblical event occurred 18,000 years ago only to find that scientists are dating the event to 145,000 years ago, the time of the previous Ice Age. Perhaps, an example of just such an event is the migration of Cain out of Africa following his banishment following the murder of Abel discussed earlier. In the earlier discussion, the archeological finding of human habitation near the Persian Gulf dating back to 125,000 years ago, I related this finding to the migration of Cain. Looking at the two periods of minimum temperatures in the last two Ice Ages, when sea levels would be at their minimums, thus facilitating migrations, we find one such minimum at 65,000 to 18,000 years ago for the last Ice Age, and at about 155,000 to

140,000 years ago for the prior Ice Age. This would correspond to an early migration, which I call Cain's migration, and a later migration corresponding to the migrations that occurred from 50,000 to 70,000 years ago.

The map in Figure 68 provides an important insight into the climate and the shape of the map. It also has a major influence on migration routes as our ancestors left Africa. There are a couple of items I would like to illuminate because they will have an impact on some of our conclusions as we compare Biblical references to modern scientific models. In regard to the first point, take a careful look at the coastlines. You will notice the vegetation coloring areas frequently slop over the modern geographic boundaries. It looks somewhat like some of my first grade coloring efforts. Actually, these reflect the more likely geographic boundaries when the huge amounts of the Earth's water are locked in massive glaciers, water level has been lowered by 400 feet, and the resulting aridity has dramatically changed patterns of vegetation. Observe in particular that the Red Sea is almost completely over grown with land vegetation and even some desert. Notice that the rain forest area of Africa touches the Red Sea, and becomes a juxtaposition of a likely habitat of our hominid ancestors and an easy crossing site for migration. Similarly, the Persian Gulf is obliterated as a body of water. Also, take special note of the eastern and western ends of the Mediterranean, Black, and Caspian Seas. You will notice that both ends are closed off by dry land because of the lower sea level. It is also likely that the boot of Italy was connected to North Africa, or nearly so, by a land bridge. These dams of land will have a significant impact on some of our conclusions. Finally, you will notice that there is no water separating Britain from the continent of Europe, and there

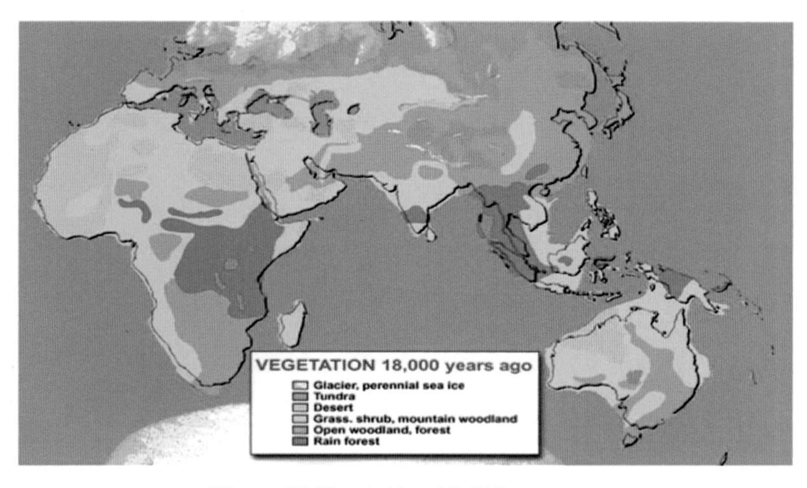

Figure 68 Vegetation 18,000 years ago

is significant dry land off the coasts of India and Japan. These will become significant facts when we encounter inundated settlements as a result of massive worldwide flooding.

One other consideration of the effects of an Ice Age has to do with rainfall. Lower temperatures and reduced water areas lead to a reduction in the amount of water evaporated into the atmosphere during an Ice Age. That means that rainfall is significantly reduced, and much of the precipitation that does occur falls as snow, which does not melt significantly, even during the summer months.

The result of these effects, in combination, is that there is little or no rain over much of the Earth during an Ice Age. In addition, what little fresh water is available comes from the runoff from melting ice near the massive glaciers. Listen to the oral traditions, which we have set down in writing in Genesis, and you will hear clear descriptions of a barren landscape with a dry climate, yet still capable of producing a bountiful source of fresh water:

> **There was no field shrub on earth and no grass of the field had sprouted, for the LORD God had sent no rain upon the earth and there was no man to till the soil, but a stream was welling up out of the earth and was watering all the surface of the ground.**

Genesis 2:5-6.

If you have ever been up close to a glacier, you will quickly notice the runoff of water beneath the glacier, as seen in Figure 69. You may also hear the ear-splitting cracks of ice breaking off. In the aridity that occurs during the depths of an Ice Age, this runoff is probably where most of the liquid water that would be available. We will see more of these hints of an Ice Age in later discussions. For now, let us look at the effect of these runoffs on migration of the human species, moving our ancestors out of Africa, from the Cradle of Life.

Figure 69 Glacial runoff

Migration of Cain

Let us pause again to put together several pieces of information which, I think, lead to another rather startling conclusion. First, we have the evidence suggesting that Mitochondrial Eve, the ancestor of females alive today, lived about 150,000 to 200,000 years ago.[206] Next, we get a piece of information moving the earliest migration out of Africa much earlier than previously thought.

As we will address later in more detail, scientists believe that humans migrated out of Africa about 50,000 to 70,000 years ago. However, a very recent find has discovered evidence of a band of humans near the shores of the Persian Gulf, all the way on the far side of the Arabian Peninsula. This find has been dated to approximately 125,000 years ago.[207] That is somewhat inconsistent with both the scientific discussion of the early migration of humans, with one exception—the case of Cain.

Cain, the first child of Adam and Eve, was marked with an identifying mark and banished. He moved out to a land east of Eden, which according to our reasoning is in Africa. Therefore, the Biblical account presents Cain as going out of Africa very early, even before the general migrations occur. This new evidence from the world of paleontology presents the scientific evidence that such an early migration had indeed happened.

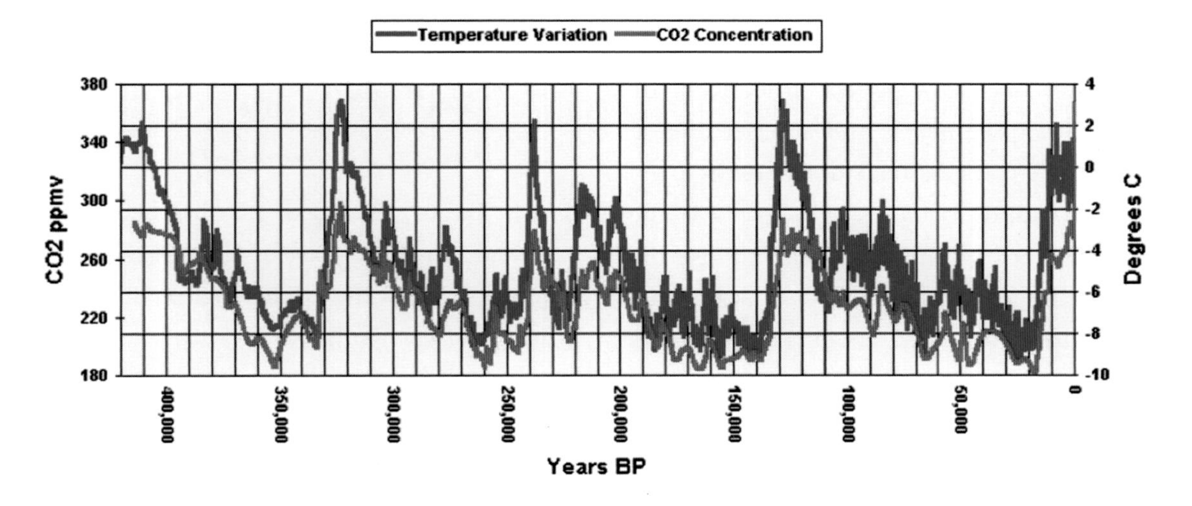

Figure 70 Ice Ages

There is another piece of evidence to support this early migration. It comes from our previous discussion of Ice Ages. Let's look again at the temperatures during the coldest part of the Ice Ages over the last 400,000 years.

We have spent most of our time up to this point talking about the last Ice Age, the one that reached it coldest temperature about 20,000 years ago, followed by the beginning of a period of global warming that began about 18,000 years ago and continues to this day. Let's take a look at the Ice Age previous to our last one. This one reached its coldest temperatures between 160,000 and 150,000 years ago. Recall that when the temperature reaches these Ice Age minimums, immense amounts of water all across the Earth is locked up in great continental glaciers. In the last Ice Age the ice was a mile thick over New York. As a consequence of these colossal glaciers, sea level dropped by hundreds of feet.

What we have is a perfect little storm of facts that fits quite neatly into another one of our Biblical stories handed down to us over tens of thousands of years ago. Eve was the Biblical mother of Cain and Abel, and also the ancestral mother of all living females today. Mitochondrial Eve lived about 150,000 years ago. The water levels of the Red Sea, along with all the other bodies of water around the Earth, would be down by hundreds of feet. This would leave the Red Sea an easily waded body of water, especially where the Red Sea meets the Gulf of Aden near Djibouti. Near the Great Hanish Island today, the maximum depth is only 154 meters[208], easily dry land in the depths of the Ice Age 140,000 years ago.

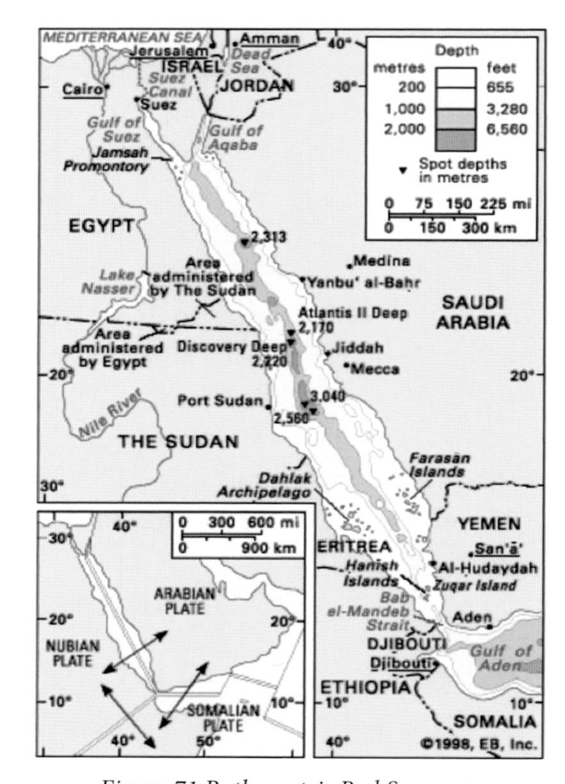

Figure 71 Bathymetric Red Sea map

So, Cain has killed his brother and is banished and he travels east. And east is precisely where the archeological site found evidence of early migration as early as 125,000 years ago.[209]

> **Cain then left the LORD'S presence and settled in the land of Nod, east of Eden.**

Genesis 4:14.

Keeping in mind that migrations were not headlong sprints from Africa to the far eastern side of Arabia. Cain, his followers, and descendants have about 25,000 years to casually move along, following the availability of food to the East Arabian camp site. Let's add yet another thought to this early migration. Looking back at Africa we see the primates left behind. We look at the modern aboriginal population of Africa. They are black. Of varying shades to be sure, but they are black.

So the LORD put a mark on Cain, lest anyone should kill him at sight. Genesis 4:14-15.

Figure 72 Migration of Cain

So if God wanted to put an identifying mark on Cain, one that would make him appear instantly recognizable, what would He do? My reasoning tells me that the mark of Cain was white. This, of course, would be quite distinctive among those he was around, thereby prompting his fear. It is not hard to identify Cain in Michele Giannetti's depiction of the migration of Cain in Figure 72. By separating himself from the black population, he removed himself from the gene pool that had started in Africa. His distinctive white color would be shared and perpetuated by those who went with him into exile.

Looking at Figure 73, if his descendants continued their migration east, bending northward along the Arabian Gulf and into the valley of the Euphrates and Tigris rivers and continuing north, they would arrive at the Caucuses Mountains, the reputed origin of Caucasians.

With few or no other humans to encounter, his band of descendants would gradually become more light-skinned as they moved farther from their ancestral home and into northern regions. And, behind them, the gateways to the east were rapidly slamming shut. Looking once more at our Ice Age temperature chart, we see the penultimate Ice Age ended about 140,000 years ago. The next 10,000, years saw the onset of global warming, causing temperatures to rise even higher than they are today. Sea levels rose precipitously hundreds of feet in that geologically "twinkling of an eye." The next Ice Age would not reach its coldest depth until 18,000 to 20,000 years ago.

Figure 73 Migration to the Caucasus

Migration out of Africa

Scientists have traced the migration routes out of Africa by analyzing and dating various fossil finds or by dating the artifacts, such as stone tools that have been discovered. They have also studied human DNA and, in particular, mitochondrial DNA. By finding genetic mutations in mitochondrial DNA that have occurred over numerous generations, particular ancestors can be traced back over migration routes all the way to Africa.[210]

Sometime between 50,000 and 70,000 years ago, a group of bold, adventurous ancestors crossed the Red Sea and settled in Asia. Crossing the Red Sea was a bit simpler than recorded in Exodus as Moses led the Israelites out of Egypt, because the last Ice Age had dramatically lowered the water level in the Red Sea. In places, it was only a few miles across so it could be easily crossed in primitive watercraft.[211] To get an idea what this may have been like for primitive humans, consider the Gandy Bridge connecting Tampa and St. Petersburg, Florida. (I chose this example because my grandfather was an engineer, and he came to Florida to work on this bridge.) The bridge spans approximately two and a half miles over Tampa Bay. Standing on one side, it is quite easy to see the far side across the bay as seen in Figure 74. For one who is intent on migrating to the lands beyond, this narrow stretch of water would be only the slightest hindrance.

Figure 74 Gandy Bridge over Tampa Bay

Once in Asia, the adventurers split into two groups. One group stayed in the Middle East while the other group pushed on, eventually reaching all the way to Eastern Asia, Japan, and the Philippines, about 50,000 years ago, as seen in Figure 75. The route is completely obscured by the sea level that has risen as the Earth's climate warmed since the end of the Ice Age.[212]

About 40,000 years ago, as the Ice Age was ebbing, the settlers began moving into Europe, and ultimately as they pushed further along, generation by generation, just crossing the next hill, they arrived in North America and even deep into South America 12,000 to 18,000 years ago.[213] While all this

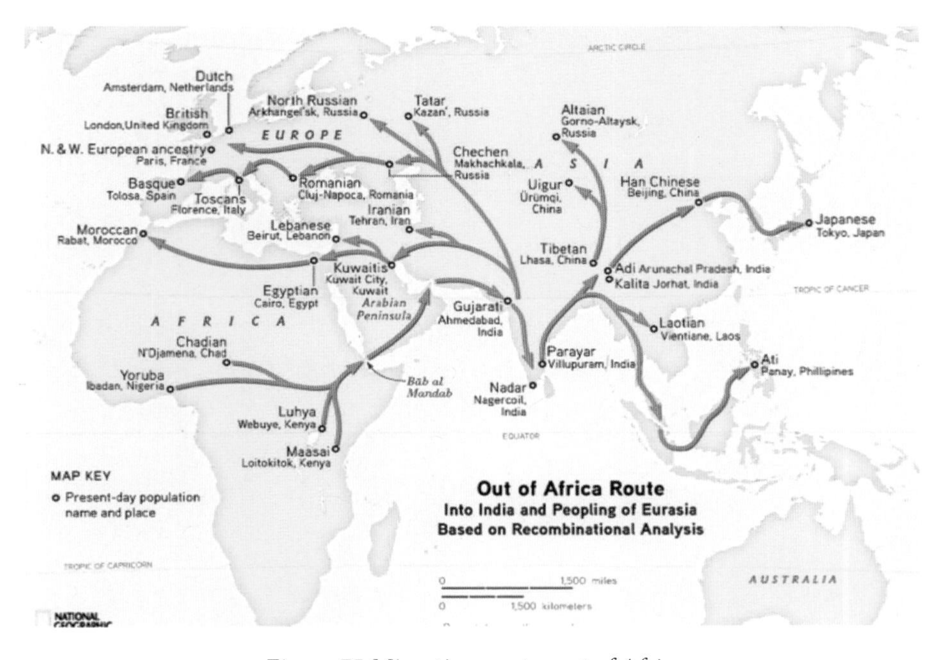

Figure 75 Migration routes out of Africa

migration around the world was going on, those who stayed behind in Africa spread out to new horizons just as their migrating kin were doing.

What then does Genesis say about these migrations? As it turns out, Genesis says something very similar, indeed. The Bible discusses the sons of Noah and their descendants and how they dispersed over the known world. This migration is depicted in Figure 76.

> **The descendants of Japheth: Gomer, Magog, Madai, Javan, Tubal, Meshech, and Tiras. The descendants of Gomer: Ashkenaz, Riphath, and Togarmah. The descendants of Javan: Elishah, Tarshish, the Kittim, and the Rodanim. These are the descendants of Japheth, and from them sprang the maritime nations, in their respective lands—each with its own language—by their clans within their nations.**

Genesis 10:2-5.

Secular and scripture scholars have identified a number of lands represented by these names. Gomer refers to the Cimmerians[214] who, according to Herodotus, lived north of the Black Sea while others locate them south of the Caucasus.[215] Madia refers to the Medes of what is now modern Iran and Javan refers to the Greeks.[216] Ashkenaz refers to the Scythians who

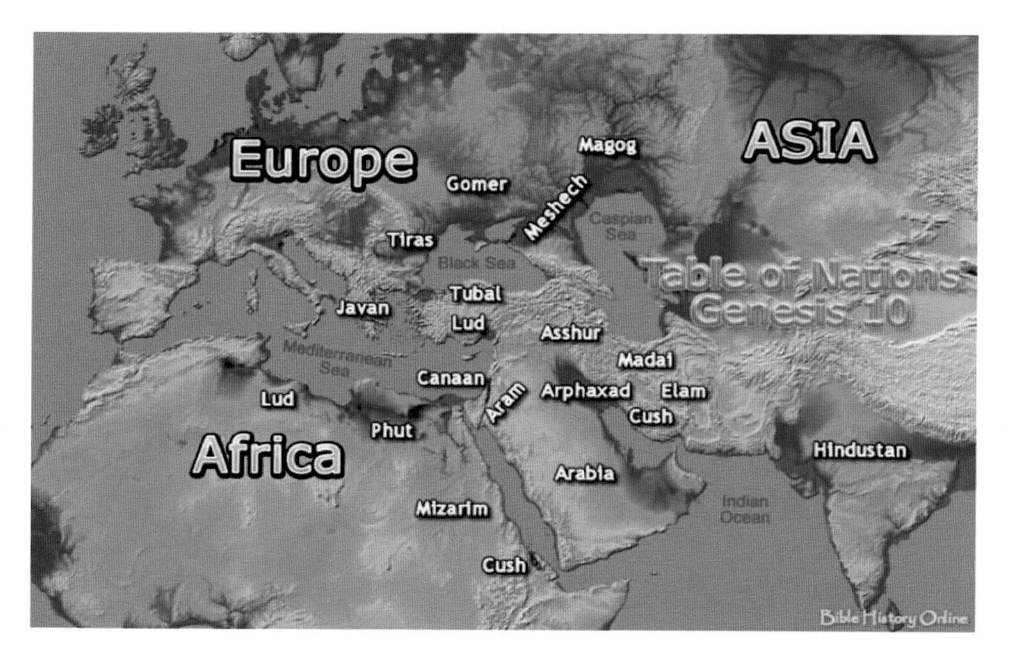

Figure 76 Migration of Noah's sons

inhabited the Caspian steppe in southern Russia.[217] Elishah and the Kittim refer to inhabitants of Cyprus and the Rodanim are inhabitants of Rhodes together populating the islands south of Greece.[218]

> **The descendants of Ham: Cush, Mizraim, Put, and Canaan. The descendants of Cush: Seba, Havilah, Sabtah, Raamah, and Sabteca. The descendants of Raamah: Sheba and Dedan.**

Genesis 10:6-7.

Scholars have identified many areas referred to by these names. Cush is in Africa along the Nile River. It includes parts of southern Egypt and northern Sudan; it may also have included territory on both sides of the Red Sea. Mizraim refers to Egypt, while Put is, according to biblical scholars, Libya or East Africa.[219]

> **The descendants of Shem: Elam, Asshur, Arpachshad, Lud, and Aram.**

Genesis 20:22.

The descendants of Shem are the Semitic peoples of the Fertile Crescent and the Arabian Peninsula. Also in the list is Aram, one of the perennial adversaries of ancient Israel. It also provided the language, Aramaic, spoken by many people, including Our Lord, who lived in the area of Israel. Another perennial adversary of ancient Israel was Assyria, represented by Shem's son Asshur.

Language

One would think that with all this migration coming from a common area, there would be a degree of commonality in the languages spoken among all these diverse groups. Indeed, Genesis has some things to say about this concept.

> **That is why it was called Babel, because there the LORD confused the speech of all the world. It was from that place that he scattered them all over the earth.**

Genesis 11:9.

In this section of Genesis we also get the story of the Tower of Babel and the dispersal of humanity over the Earth and the diversification of languages. From a faith perspective, all of this addresses the fulfillment of God's command to go forth and fill the Earth.[220]

> **God blessed them, saying: "Be fertile and multiply; fill the earth and subdue it."**

Genesis 1:28.

But, as usual, we see the Bible presenting a theological message by using real people and events. The event described is the migration of humans out of Africa, by stages into the Middle East and, from there, into Europe, along the Asian coast, and into the rest of the world. The Biblical vehicle is genealogical, but the message

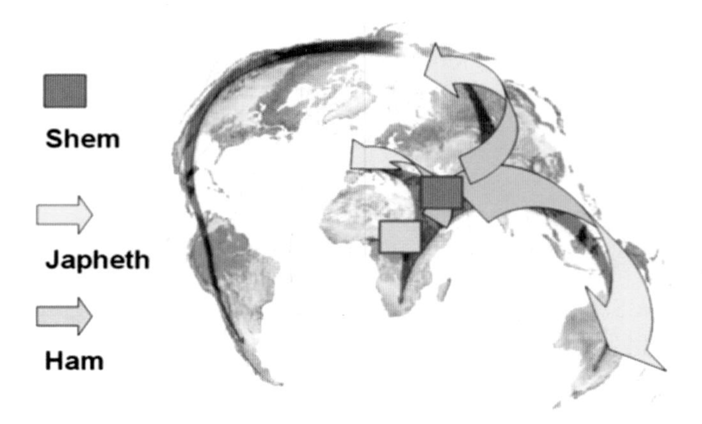

Figure 77 Human migration routes

is human migration. In fact, if we overlay the descriptions of Noah's descendants and the lands they represent, and extend them over the human migration routes presented in the National Geographic representation of mitochondrial DNA studies, the results are quite similar, as seen in Figure 77.

There is another aspect of the Tower of Babel account that needs to be considered as it relates to oral traditions and the Bible. Frequently in the Bible, we will see the same story told twice with variations in the account. We saw this in the creation of man narrative.

> **God created man in his image; in the divine image he created him; male and female he created them.**

Genesis 1:27.

> **The LORD God formed man out of the clay of the ground and blew into his nostrils the breath of life, and so man became a living being.**

Genesis 2:7.

Generally, this represents the telling of the same story from two or more oral traditions. Typically, the Bible does not try to reconcile differences in stories to present one coherent narrative. Rather, it presents each on its own, almost like having two witnesses tell independent stories from their own perspective, including events viewed as significant while omitting other aspects of the story. With these multiple oral tradition sources, we are able to gather a more complete understanding of the events that occurred. So it is with the migration out of Africa narrative. One oral tradition presents the story from the perspective of the descendants of Noah.

While the other oral tradition presents the event from the perspective of the hubris of mankind and the development of languages. One thing we cannot determine from these two narratives is whether they actually describe the same migration out of Africa or two separate waves of migrations that scientists hypothesize

Hominid Interspecies Encounters

Recalling that the Bible teaches theological and moral truths using the examples of real people and real places makes our look at the events surrounding the flood much easier to understand. The Bible sets the stage for its discussion of the flood with a curious little narrative that bears closer scrutiny "through the eyes of faith."

> **When men began to multiply on earth and daughters were born to them, the sons of heaven saw how beautiful the daughters of man were, and so they took for their wives as many of them as they chose. At that time the Nephilim appeared on earth (as well as later), after the sons of heaven had intercourse with the daughters of man, who bore them sons. They were the heroes of old, the men of renown. When the LORD saw how great was man's wickedness on earth, and how no desire that his heart conceived was ever anything but evil, he regretted that he had made man on the earth, and his heart was grieved.**

Genesis 6:1-2, 3-6.

The New American Bible adds a couple of footnotes to help us with our understanding of the passage:

> 1 [1-4] This is apparently a fragment of an old legend that had borrowed much from ancient mythology. The sacred author incorporates it here, not only in order to account for the prehistoric giants of Palestine, whom the Israelites called the Nephilim, but also to introduce the story of the flood with a moral orientation—the constantly increasing wickedness of mankind.
>
> 2 [2] The sons of heaven: literally "the sons of the gods" or "the sons of God," i.e., the celestial beings of mythology.

Dr. Schroeder notes,

> "The word Nephilim comes from the Hebrew root for fallen or inferior. Adam, having a *neshema,* would find the Cro-Magnon inferior in spirit if not in body."[221]

In addition, William Barclay, in his Daily Bible Study of the Gospel of St. Matthew, adds some explanatory remarks that may also shed some on light the events and people involved.

> The King James Version says that the peace-makers shall be called the children of God; the Greek more literally is that the peace-makers will be called the sons *huioi*, of God. This is a typical Hebrew way of expression. Hebrew is not rich in adjectives, and often when Hebrew wishes to describe something, it uses, not an adjective, but the phrase son of... plus an

> abstract noun. Hence a man may be called a son of peace instead of a peaceful man. Barnabas is called a son of consolation instead of a consoling and comforting man. This beatitude says: Blessed are the peace-makers, for they shall be called the sons of God; what it means is: Blessed are the peace-makers, for they shall be doing a God-like work. The man who makes peace is engaged on the very work which the God of peace is doing.

If we apply William Barclay's analysis to the phrase "sons of heaven," we arrive at a description of men who are heavenly-looking or heavenly-acting. The idea that these men were acting in a heavenly way is eliminated because of the Lord's observation of how great was man's wickedness in this context. Let us now put this information from the Bible and Biblical scholars together with current scientific understanding of the state of the early Paleolithic human species. When we do so, I think that we will find another example of the Bible capturing, from exceedingly ancient oral traditions, events concerning encounters between hominid species.

There is a period in relatively recent (in a geological sense) human development of four hominid species coexisting during the same time frame. When a species becomes extinct, sometimes it occurs suddenly due to some cataclysmic event, but more often it occurs over a period of time, slowly dying away as its environment becomes inhospitable or it loses out in the competition for food to more adapted species. Thus during the time when Homo Erectus, Homo Neanderthal, and Homo Sapiens and our immediate ancestor Homo Heidelbergensis, coexisted as shown in Figure 78, the first two species were in the period of decline before extinction. Yet, all three could, and many scientists believe, did have mutual encounters. In fact, recent DNA findings confirm that most modern humans today have a small amount of Neanderthal DNA. The findings indicate that the interbreeding occurred about 45,000 to 80,000 years ago.[222] As

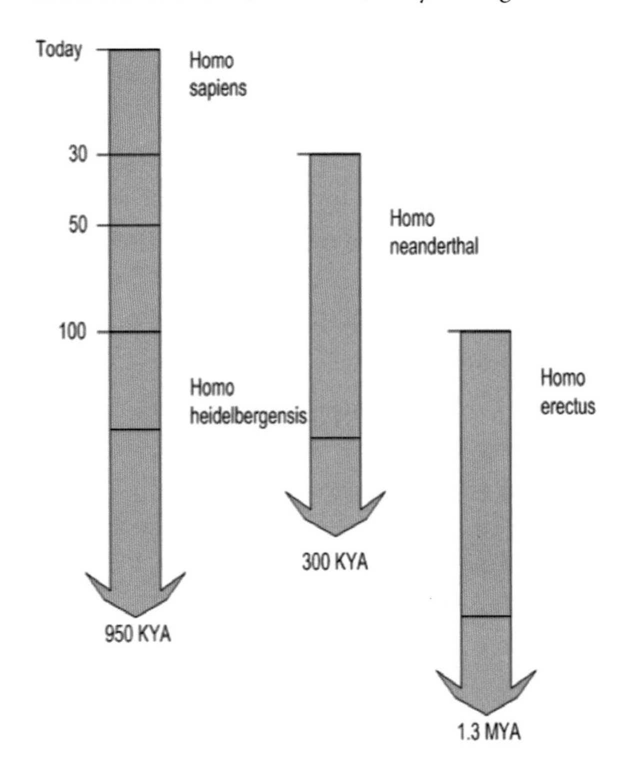

Figure 78 Hominid interspecies encounters

often happens in human encounters with less advanced creatures or even civilizations, the less advanced do not fare very well. Take as examples the extinction at human hands of the Carolina parakeet, the dodo bird, and the carrier pigeon in the animal kingdom. Though once thriving in huge numbers, all three were hunted to extinction by human beings. Among civilizations, consider the Native American encounters with more technologically advanced and, probably more importantly, more disease resistant early European explorers of the American continents. The result was complete extinction of numerous native cultures including the Aztecs, Incas, and Caribe tribes.

Returning to our Paleolithic ancestors, a comparison of time lines over the last 750 thousand years shows the overlap. One interesting characteristic variation among these coexisting Homo species is average height. Neanderthal man was the shortest of the group averaging about 65 inches for the males. Our immediate ancestors, Heidelberg man averaged about 69 inches which is about the same as modern American humans. Homo erectus reached a height of 73 inches, although, this is not the average. Human height is highly dependent on diet and nutrition. In North Korea, for example, the average height of males is only 64 inches. Humans in the middle ages averaged about 68 inches but that declined to 65 inches in the 17th and 18th Centuries.

The reason for the height discussion is the Biblical references to Nephilim and the "heroes of old" are possible clues about which species may have been involved in these encounters. Clearly, Homo Erectus was significantly taller than Neanderthal man and may have been considered a giant, but the latter was stockier and more powerfully built. It is likely that these encounters between Homo species are what have been captured in this curious passage of the Bible. There are numerous examples of Biblical characters encountering what they perceived to be giants. Perhaps the best known is the story of David and Goliath depicted in Figure 79.

Figure 79 David and Goliath

A champion named Goliath of Gath came out from the Philistine camp; he was six and a half feet tall.

1 Samuel 17:4.

Today, just board an airplane, as I once did, at the same time as a college basketball team and you will get an idea of what the army of Israel felt as they faced the taunts of Goliath. Perhaps more aptly described are the reports from Moses' spies as they reconnoitered the Promised Land soon after their exodus from Egypt.

And all the people we saw there are huge men, veritable giants (the Anakim were a race of giants); we felt like mere grasshoppers, and so we must have seemed to them."

Numbers 13:32-33.

I think it is reasonable that the Anakim and Goliath were remnants of the fading Homo Erectus or other hominid species that eventually passed from existence. I also think that these encounters have been recalled through oral traditions that have come down to us as folk tales today. I strongly suspect such creatures as trolls, giants, and ogres come to us from just such encounters. I also think that some of ancient legends, such as Beowulf versus Grendel and Gilgamesh with his companion, the wild man Ekidu, depicted in Figure 80, are based on the same inter-Homo species encounters. It is also highly likely that these encounters were not peaceful, but consisted of abductions, rapes, and enslavement.

Figure 80 Scene from Beowulf

Gilgamesh and his "wild man" companion, Ekidu

THE GREAT FLOOD

The Great Flood story in Genesis is another one of those Bible Stories that we heard as children, but as we grew older, we concluded that the story was simply a tale told to impart some theological message with no basis in historical fact. Some argue that the writers of the Old Testament, while living in captivity in Babylon in the 6th century BC, adapted Sumerian legends of a great flood to impart their theological message. While that is a possibility, research by H. S. Bellamy indicates that there are more than 500 legends worldwide about a great flood. Ancient civilizations such as China, Babylonia, Wales, Russia, India, America, Hawaii, Scandinavia, Sumatra, Peru, and Polynesia all have their own versions of a giant flood.[223] This fact, along with the scientific data from research on Ice Ages indicates that there was indeed a catastrophic worldwide flood, or perhaps more accurately, there were worldwide floods following each Ice Age. While the story's purpose of imparting a theological truth is certainly correct, I think there is strong evidence supporting the historical basis for the story of Noah and the Great Flood.

> **It was on that day that all the fountains of the great abyss burst forth, and the floodgates of the sky were opened. For forty days and forty nights heavy rain poured down on the earth.**

Genesis 7:11-12.

This is another story captured by the Bible of oral traditions handed down from generation to generation that is about real people and real events that actually happened. There is also an indication that this story did not come from a single oral source, but from several different sources. For example, the fact that it rained for forty days and forty nights is mentioned three times in chapter 7 of Genesis i.e. verses 4, 12, and 17.

> **Seven days from now I will bring rain down on the earth for forty days and forty nights, and so I will wipe out from the surface of the earth every moving creature that I have made.**

Genesis 7:4.

> **For forty days and forty nights heavy rain poured down on the earth.**

Genesis 7:12.

> **The flood continued upon the earth for forty days.**

Genesis 7:17.

As you read through the descriptions of the flood, it will begin to seem somewhat repetitive with some variations in the details. For example, in chapter 8 verse 4 we read that the Ark came to rest on the mountains of Arrarat, yet in the next verse it says that two months later the tops of the mountains appeared.

> **In the seventh month, on the seventeenth day of the month, the ark came to rest on the mountains of Ararat.**

Genesis 8:4.

> **On the first day of the tenth month the tops of the mountains appeared.**

Genesis 8:5.

We also need to keep in mind that in the Bible, numbers frequently have symbolic meanings and may not represent an exact count. The number forty typically represents a long period of time necessary to complete God's purpose. Such is the case of the description of the flood. Forty days and nights of heavy rain indicates an extended period of rain to achieve the flood desired by God. I think that the real key to understanding the physical reality of the flood and its correspondence to modern scientific findings is the first part of the sentence in chapter 7, verse 11.

> **It was on that day that all the fountains of the great abyss burst forth.**

Genesis 7:11.

Consider this sentence in the light of the period of warming following the depths of an Ice Age. In the last Ice Age, New York was covered by ice more than a mile thick. The basins of the Great Lakes were scooped out of the Earth by gigantic glaciers, and when all this ice melted and the glaciers retreated hundreds of miles, the Great Lakes were filled and the sea level was raised by as much as 400 feet over the entire Earth. These dramatically rising sea levels are exactly what Genesis is describing when it says "all the fountains of the great abyss burst forth."

To understand this we need to take a much closer look at the information we have concerning the Ice Ages, especially after the temperatures reached their nadir and began a

20,000 year period of global warming that continues to the present day. The effect of this period of global warming was a major rise in sea levels as the glaciers melted and ran down to the seas, just as many scientists today predict as global temperatures continue their rise that began at the end of the last Ice Age. In addition, water released from the glaciers became available for evaporation causing rainfall to increase. This accounts for the forty days and nights (extended period to fulfill God's purpose) of heavy rain; rain that had been extremely scarce during the depths of the Ice Age. You may be tempted to say that a rise of sea levels of 400 feet over a period of some 15,000 years was not all that rapid and human beings could have easily adapted.

On the graph in Figure 81 at the region marked MWP-1A, standing for Mid-Pliocene Warm Period, you see a steep slope at about 14,000 years ago that indicates a period of rapidly rising sea levels. Since it occurs over a period of years, it is not quite like standing on the sea shore watching a tsunami wash over the coast line. There are, instead, two dramatic effects that would have catastrophic effects on Stone Age people living at water's edge or at least near to the water. Consider, also, that living near water would be very desirable for Stone Age people because of the availability of food. The first effect is a gradual increase in water levels forcing continual moves to higher

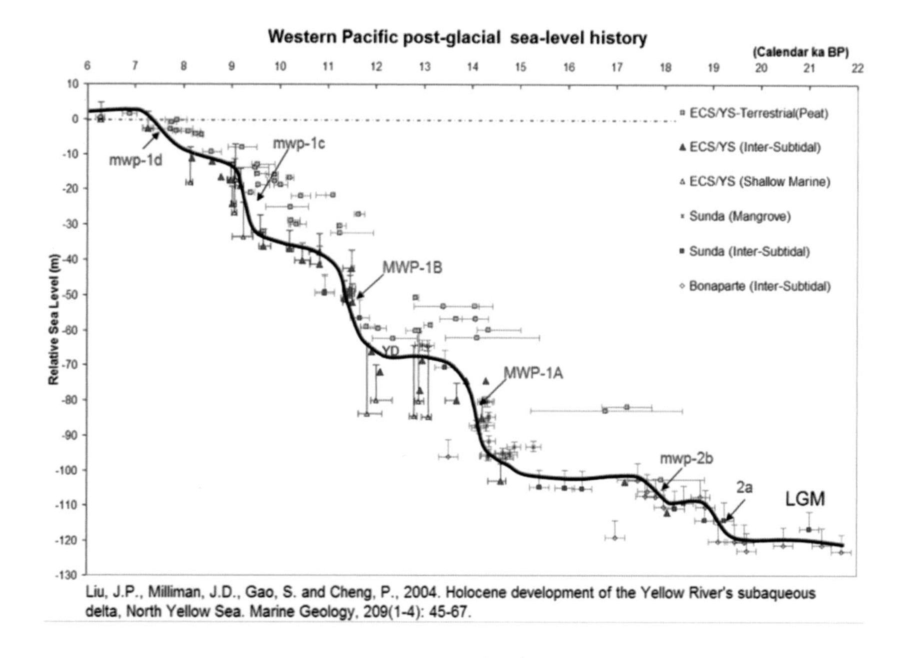

Figure 81 Sea levels rise

ground. Since I am from Florida, I will use the Florida landscape to illustrate the effects of a continual rise in water level over a number of years to primitive people.

My son has a home at the water's edge of Tampa Bay. On a nice day, he could lower his boat into the water to go for an afternoon cruise or spend the day enjoying the abundant fishing in the bay. His house sits about five to seven feet above the high tide mark on a normal day. However, during hurricane season, he may have to leave the house and move in with my wife and me until the storm passes. Our house is about 32 feet above mean sea level.

Now, picture yourself living where my son's house is 14,000 years ago. In Florida, we would be many hundreds of miles from any melting glaciers so we wouldn't see much direct effect. Rather you would notice that each year the water level is definitely higher than the year before. The water would just seem to be rising out of the deep, the abyss, and getting higher all the time. Over a period of a year or two, perhaps less, the water would be lapping at the edge of your hut and you would simply have to move. So you would pack up you family and belongings and move further inland setting up your new homestead not far from ours which is some 32 feet above sea level. This would be quite satisfactory for a few years, but soon we would notice the swamps, lakes, and ponds in the area seem to be getting higher. After, the rainy season the water levels never seem to drop and everything is overflowing its banks. In fact, some of the lakes have merged cutting off pathways between them. Eventually, it becomes evident that we, too, must move to higher ground. So now the whole family begins moving inland. It is more difficult now than similar travels in the past because streams have become rivers, lakes and ponds are everywhere forcing us to back track frequently to find a way to higher ground.

Unbeknownst to us, the entire coast line is gradually, but apace, receding as the sea levels continue their rise. This process continues over a number of years forcing us to periodically pack up the household and move ever further inland to higher ground. Eventually, we make our way to the ridge backbone of the state near what is now Lake Wales. There we find Iron Mountain, the highest point in the peninsula of Florida. It rises 289 feet above sea level. There we think we will be safe, but that becomes an illusion. For one thing other families are just like us, forced by the inexorably rising water levels to seek ever higher ground. As we make our way up Iron Mountain, we notice that not everyone appears to be happy with our arrival. There seems to be enough space to go around and there seems to be plenty of game to provide food for the family. That, however, is part of the illusion. While many animals have had to seek higher ground just as we did, many did not find a safe passage and have been washed away. In addition, constantly arriving groups of people find the competition for food a source of constant irritation.

To get a better view of the situation, we climb to the very summit of Iron Mountain seen in Figure 82. Today we could climb the stairs to the top of Bok Tower for a magnificent view of the countryside, but that will have to wait a few thousand years. Nevertheless, we arrive at the summit and look out on all sides. We are astonished to see that we are on an island. The water level has been rising all these years, and now we are completely surrounded,

Figure 82 Bok Tower on Iron Mountain

and the water just keeps rising. Perhaps, we could build a raft of logs, but, where would we go? Beyond the water level lapping at the base of this mountain, rising higher and higher each month, we can see nothing but water.

All the areas we traveled through on our way here are now completely submerged. All we can do is look out in every direction and see slowly but steadily rising water. Sadly, this tale has no happy ending. The water levels at the end of the Ice Age will rise some 400 feet, and Florida's mightiest mountain will become nothing but a gentle rise at the bottom of the now conjoined Gulf of Mexico and Atlantic Ocean. The closest land is hundreds of miles away in Georgia and Alabama where, even there, this fatal trap of reaching high ground, only to be surrounded by ever rising water is played out time and again.

Now this tale is somewhat fanciful because the waters have already risen their 400 feet since the last Ice Age, and the Iron Mountain still stands majestically (for us Floridians at least) above the surrounding landscape, providing a haven for those seeking higher ground—not very many I suspect. But the idea of bands of people and animals, struggling for survival, with only the faintest glimpse of a fledgling civilization, having to seek higher ground, and finding themselves cut off, stranded on newly made islands that are ultimately submerged, was undoubtedly a common fate for many who had once enjoyed the abundant food supplies available at the water's edge.

The second scenario is just as likely but with a much more sudden and catastrophic sequence of events. Picture the Mediterranean Sea as it might look with the water level 400 feet lower than it is today. The map in Figure 83 is a bathymetric map of the Mediterranean Sea from the United States Oceanic and Atmospheric Administration (NOAA). Over this map, I have superimposed a green shoreline at the 400 feet depth level. This approximately represents what the map of the Mediterranean Sea would look like 18,000 years ago at the nadir of the last Ice Age. From this representation, it is clear that both the Strait of Gibraltar (point A) at the western end of the Mediterranean Sea and the Dardanelles Strait (point B) at the eastern entrance are blocked off. Moreover, the boot of Italy and the island of Sicily connect to the coast line of North Africa. Indeed, virtually all of the islands that exist today are connected to the shore line and a few islands have appeared out of the water that are completely submerged today. Humans living during this period would undoubtedly have taken advantage of the food sources present by the water's edge. This would have caused them to establish their villages and settlements far out into what is today's Mediterranean Sea.

As the sea levels began to rise due to the glacial melting caused by the global warming following the lowest temperatures during the last Ice Age, the same series of events described previously in the Iron Mountain scenario would likely have occurred. Indeed, those islands in the Mediterranean Sea that are submerged today would be precisely the kinds of traps that would lure human villagers to ever higher ground, only to have even the high ground

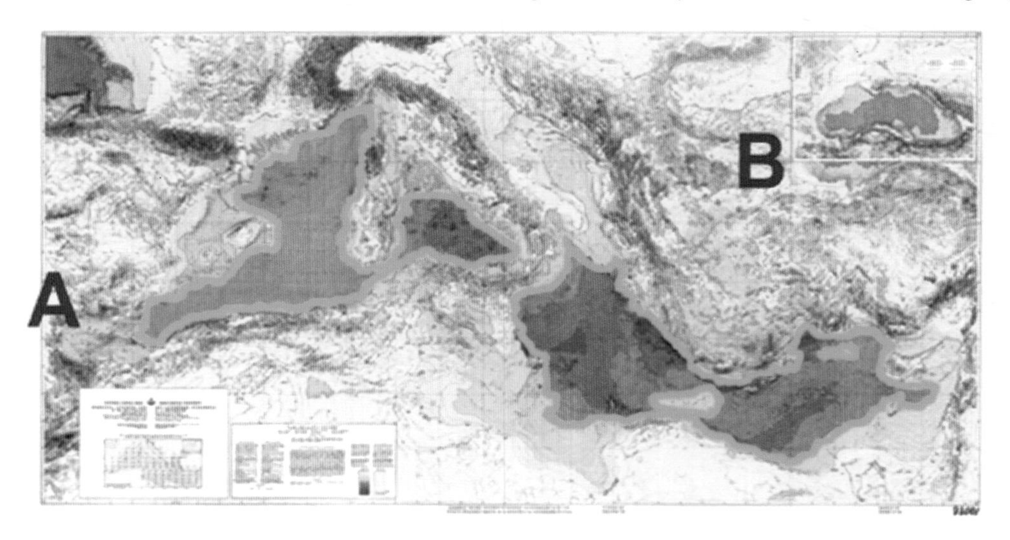

Figure 83 Mediterranean Basin with 400 foot lower sea level

submerged with disastrous consequences.

The blocked entrances at the Eastern and Western entrances would have caused an even greater, more sudden catastrophe. As the world sea levels continued to rise, it is likely that the Atlantic Ocean level would have risen much faster than the Mediterranean Sea because of the greater number of sources of glacial run off. However, once the sea level at the Strait of Gibraltar breached the top of the land levee, blocking the Atlantic Ocean from the Mediterranean Sea Basin, it would begin to pour in with ever increasing volume. The water rushing through the strait would begin cutting through the land, levee eroding it away in much the same way as the Grand Canyon was formed. The result of this land levee breach and consequent deepening erosion would create a sudden, tsunami-like effect very rapidly filling the Western Mediterranean Sea Basin to the same level as the Atlantic Ocean. Likewise, the Black Sea would eventually cut through the Dardanelles Strait rapidly flooding the Eastern Mediterranean Sea Basin.

The rapidity with which the seabed would have been flooded would be an utter catastrophe for Stone Age residents of the Mediterranean Sea Basin. They would have had little chance of escape, and virtually every living thing living on the land in the Basin would have perished in the flood. The description in Genesis of this event captures the magnitude of the disaster.

> **Higher and higher above the earth rose the waters, until all the highest mountains everywhere were submerged, the crest rising fifteen cubits higher than the submerged mountains. All creatures that stirred on earth perished: birds, cattle, wild animals, and all that swarmed on the earth, as well as all mankind. Everything on dry land with the faintest breath of life in its nostrils died out. The LORD wiped out every living thing on earth: man and cattle, the creeping things and the birds of the air; all were wiped out from the earth.**

Genesis 7:19-23.

It is not necessary to suppose that "every" living thing had to die in the literal sense of this passage to have very reasonable description of the Great Flood event that happened to real people. From the perspective of those living in or near the Mediterranean Sea Basin, this description would have been quite appropriate. As the torrent from the breach of the land bridge between Spain and Africa at Gibraltar was breached and the hundreds of feet sea level differential between the Atlantic Ocean and the Mediterranean Basin began to be equalized in a matter of days, the description is frightfully accurate. Look again at the map in Figure 83. Everything living near the seashore represented by the green 400 foot boundary would be washed away as the water levels sought their normal sea shore boundaries where blue meets browns on the map.

There is another description of a very similar event from ancient sources. In approximately 360 BC, Plato wrote the dialogue, *Critas,* in which he described Atlantis. The information for this dialogue had been passed down as oral tradition from his grandfather. The story of Atlantis was to have taken place about 9600 BC. This date would place it near the midpoint of the time between the nadir of the last Ice Age and today—certainly a time of rapidly increasing sea levels. Atlantis was described as a great naval power near the Pillars of Hercules—the Strait of Gibraltar. This would have placed it along the sea shore of the Mediterranean Sea Basin at a time of severely depressed sea levels. As the rising Atlantic Ocean breached the great levee separating it from the Mediterranean Sea Basin, Atlantis would not have sunk so much as it would have been inundated by the rapid filling of the Mediterranean Sea Basin. The distinction would have been small comfort to the citizens of Atlantis. One may note that the depiction of Atlantis in Figure 84 would be more representative of Plato's description in the 4th century BC than the actual city of 9600 BC.

Figure 84 Plato's Atlantis

If these descriptions of rising sea levels caused by the retreat of the Ice Age are correct, it is reasonable to expect some submerged Stone Age archeological sites would have been discovered. While no sign of a great civilization that might be Atlantis has been found, there is evidence of submerged Stone Age settlements. In 2007, an 8000 year old settlement was discovered under the English Channel, just off the coast of the Isle of Wight.[224]

> This is a site of international importance as it reveals a time before the English Channel existed when Europe and Britain were linked. Earlier excavations have produced flint tools, pristine 8,000-year-old organic material such as acorns, charcoal and worked pieces of wood showing evidence of extensive human activity...At first we had no idea of the size of this site, but now we are finding

evidence of hearths and ovens so it appears to be an extensive settlement.

Another Ice Age settled area that has been discovered beneath the North Sea is known as Doggerland. It was described in *Science & Tech* magazine as:

> Doggerland, a huge area of dry land that stretched from Scotland to Denmark was slowly submerged by water between 18,000 BC and 5,500 BC.
>
> Divers from oil companies have found remains of a 'drowned world' with a population of tens of thousands—which might once have been the 'real heartland' of Europe.225

The descriptions of the inundation of Doggerland are similar to the prior descriptions of the Mediterranean Basin and the Black Sea Basin described above.

During the most recent glaciation, the Last Glacial Maximum that ended in this area around 18,000 years ago, the North Sea and almost all of the British Isles were covered with glacial ice and the sea level was about 120 m (390 ft) lower than it is today. After that the climate became warmer and during the Late Glacial Maximum much of the North Sea and English Channel was an expanse of low-lying tundra, extending around 12,000 BCE as far as the modern northern point of Scotland.[226]

Evidence including the contours of the present seabed shows that after the first main Ice Age the watershed between North Sea drainage and English Channel drainage extended east from East Anglia then southeast to the Hook of Holland, not across the Strait of Dover, and that the Thames, Meuse, Scheldt and Rhine rivers joined and flowed along the English Channel dry bed as a wide slow river which at times flowed far before reaching the Atlantic Ocean.[227]

At about 8000 BCE, the north-facing coastal area of Doggerland had a coastline of lagoons, saltmarshes, mudflats, beaches, inland streams, rivers, marshes, and sometimes lakes. It may have been the richest hunting, fowling, and fishing ground in Europe, available to the Mesolithic culture of the time.[228]

Figure 85 Doggerland

As sea levels rose after the end of the last glacial period of the current ice age, Doggerland became submerged beneath the North Sea, cutting off what was previously the British peninsula from the European mainland by around 6500 BCE. The Dogger Bank, which had been an upland area of Doggerland, is believed to have remained as an island until at least 5000 BCE, when it flooded completely.[229]

Figure 86 Submerged town off Laconia

There is the discovery of a submerged settlement made in 1967 off the southern Laconia coast of Greece seen in Figure 86. This settlement dates from the Final Neolithic period and was occupied at least 5000 years ago.[230] On the other side of the world, a Stone Age structure, with accompanying evidence of roads and companion structures, was discovered in 100 feet of water off the coast of Okinawa, Japan. The principal structure is a rectangular stone ziggurat, seen in Figure 87, which is 600 feet wide by ninety feet high. It has been dated to between 10,000 and 12,000 years ago. Archeologists believe the site was inundated at the end of the last Ice Age.[231]

Yet another submerged village, this one inland, was discovered beneath Lake Bracciano twenty miles north of Rome. This village, known as La Marmotta, was occupied around 5700 BC, five millennia before the founding of Rome. The buildings were built on foot thick pilings driven seven feet into the ground. But, as with other post Ice Age settlements, the water level of the lake rose more than 25 feet, effectively drowning the village. It was abandoned about 5230 BC. The village is now buried in mud 400 yards off the lake shore.[232]

These discoveries of post Ice Age discoveries are examples of areas where people lived that were submerged as a result of rising waters from the melting glaciers, or as described in Genesis,

> **All the fountains of the great abyss burst forth, and the floodgates of the sky were opened.**

Genesis 7:11.

There is yet another effect of rising water during an interglacial warming period—it divides the land. Consider someone living along the seashore near the Strait of Gibraltar or the

Figure 87 Submerged ziggurat off Okinawa

Dardanelles after the land bridge has been cut through by rising waters. Each day this coastal resident walks to the shore and notices that, gradually, the water level is still rising. The water is a little farther up each day, and as he looks across the way, opposite shore seems to be slipping farther into the distance. Indeed, the straits are widening as the water is rising. But, to the man standing on the shore over a period of time, perhaps years, the opposite land would appear to be ever so gradually moving away—the land would in the process of being divided.

There is a curious comment in Genesis about a descendant of Noah named Peleg:

> **To Eber two sons were born: the name of the first was Peleg, for in his time the world was divided.**

Genesis 10:25.

There is also a footnote in the New American Bible connecting a dividing world with our earliest civilizations::

> In the Hebrew text there is a play on the name Peleg and the word *niplega*, which means "was divided."[233]

The division of the land did not go unnoticed by our ancient ancestors and, once again, the stories passed down over at least 10,000 years were kept and captured in the Holy Scripture.

Figure 88 La Marmotta, north of Rome

Noah and the Ark

Now consider a man living in the Mediterranean Sea Basin or any of these submerged areas. He is inspired by God to build a large boat on some nearby hilltop. The boat is large enough to take care of himself and his immediate family, together with food supplies and his herds of domesticated animals. But even then, it seems considerably larger than necessary. Not only that, but his neighbors observe with some snickering that Noah has not built his boat anywhere near the water, and it is much too large to drag to the nearest seashore. Naturally, he becomes the subject of much ridicule and derision, for indeed, as described in Genesis it was a huge boat, perhaps more of a barge than a boat, but, huge nevertheless. Indeed, several replicas, built to Biblical dimensions have been constructed such as the one in the Netherlands depicted in Figure 89. To get an idea of how big the Ark really was, consider parking it in Ben Hill Griffin Stadium, home of the University of Florida Gators in Gainesville, Florida depicted in Figure 90. The Ark would fill the entire length of the field plus both end zones and would go up into the end zone stands. It would be about one half the width of the playing field and stand as tall as a four story building. The Bible refers to the construction material as gopherwood, but there is a great deal of uncertainty about that reference.

> **Make yourself an ark of gopherwood, put various compartments in it, and cover it inside and out with pitch.**

Genesis 6:14.

The Septuagint translation is *xylon tetragonon* or squared timber.[234] The *Jewish Encyclopedia* believes it was most likely a translation of the Babylonian *gushure i÷ erini* (cedar-beams), or the Assyrian *giparu* (reed).[235]

Figure 89 Replica of Noah's Ark

Figure 90 Ben Hill Griffin Stadium

There is also the suggestion that, due to a similarity between the Hebrew letters for P and K, "kopherwood" would be pitched wood, as the latter half of the verse might suggest. The Genesis passage mention of pitch would indicate some knowledge of boat building, because in ancient (indeed in not so ancient times) pitch was used to seal the hulls of ships.

Earlier, I mentioned that my grandfather had come to Florida to help with the construction of Gandy Bridge across Tampa Bay, connecting Tampa with St. Petersburg. Unfortunately, my grandfather's employment may have come somewhat at the expense of my wife's great grandfather. He was an experienced steamboat captain ferrying Union troops around the Mississippi and Ohio rivers during the Civil War. He came to Tampa near the end of the 19th Century, plying his trade sailing steamboats across Tampa Bay between Tampa, St. Petersburg, and Sarasota. My wife's father told of walking through the shipyard with his grandfather who told him how leaks were sealed in their boats with pitch soaked rope that was pounded into cracks in the ship's hull using a mallet and a wooden wedge. My wife's grandfather gave her father one of the wooden wedges which he treasured for many years.

In ancient times, in southwestern India, a very large wooden boat called an Uru that had a transportation capacity of 400 tons was built and used by Arabs and Greeks as a trading vessel. These mammoth ships were constructed using teak wood without any iron or blueprints.[236] While these ships came much later than Noah's time, the construction techniques may have been similar. Given the gargantuan size of the Ark, we pause to consider how an early Stone Age man could have built such a boat even with the help of his family. Consider that the only tools available to a post-Ice Age Noah would have been stone tools. Even allowing for the possibility of exaggeration in the Ark's size, it would have taken years to build, perhaps, decades.

But, perhaps, that is just the Biblical point. While telling stories about real events and real people, the focus of the Bible is a theological message. It tells something about God and our relationship to Him. In this case, that message may very well be patience, the patience and forbearance of God. Those decades that Noah spent building the Ark were also decades for a fallen world to turn back to the Lord and be saved. We see this over and over in the Bible. God promised a land to Abraham that he would be able to call his own. It would not be until the time of King David and his son, King Solomon, more than a thousand years later, that descendants of Abram would fully possess the Promised Land, and that possession would be fleeting. Again, God would promise King David an heir to his throne who would reign forever, the long hoped for Messiah. Again it would be a thousand years before the Incarnation of Our Lord Jesus Christ would fulfill God's promise and the oracles of the prophets of the Messiah. Yet, again, the Lord promised that he would return: the Second Coming, the Parousia. Two thousand years later we are still faithfully hopeful and awaiting that blessed event. During all these periods of waiting, there has been sin and degradation followed by periods of renewal and hope for salvation. We believe to this day that our hope is not in vain.

However, for the people of Noah's time, eventually the fateful day comes. People begin to notice water levels rising, forcing everyone to higher ground. Eventually, Noah's little hilltop is surrounded by water, and the water is still rising. At this point, Noah observes a new and somewhat disturbing development.

Noah understood his inspiration from God that he should build a boat large enough for two of every animal. Being a somewhat reasonable person, he assumed he was to take his domesticated animals. But, being somewhat familiar with the dangers of the hunt, he could not quite imagine how he would capture one of these ferocious wild beasts and bring it back to his boat, much less two of each. Noah need not have worried. As the water levels continued to rise ever more rapidly, all the wild animals of the surrounding area moved in constantly increasing numbers toward the high ground where Noah's Ark lay. Picture the animal's fleeing the forest fire in Walt Disney's portrayal of *Bambi* to get an idea of the race of the local fauna toward higher ground and Noah's Ark.

So, in God's providence, He provided the mechanism that would bring the wild animals to Noah. No grand safari would have been required. Indeed, I strongly suspect that Noah's real problem would not have been bringing wild animals to his Ark; it would have been keeping too many from getting in. His big boat sitting on the hilltop would have been just the sanctuary the animals were seeking. I am certain they would not have been shy about taking advantage of it, as Michele Giannetti captured in Figure 91.

Of course, finally, the day would come that the water level rose to the Ark, and it lifted off its ever shrinking and finally disappearing hilltop. Any remaining people would have desperately tried to board the Ark, as in some doomsday scenario of a nuclear apocalypse with people seeking entrance into someone's long prepared bomb shelter. Likewise, the remaining animals would seek entrance for their survival. In the end, all would be washed away as the Ark drifted toward an eventual landfall.

While this scenario is admittedly a product of my imagination, I think it represents a reasonable description of events that would have happened to real people and real animals during those days of rapidly rising waters after the Ice Age. I also think the story of Noah that we read in the Bible has been handed down to us over countless generations in more than one oral ptradition until it was finally redacted into what we now read in the Book of Genesis. And,

Figure 91 Wild animals scramble to the Ark

nowhere in my imaginative presentation or in the more literary and poetic presentation found in the Bible do I believe there is any exclusion of the divine hand of God, working His Will in ways that are now observable and recorded in modern scientific discoveries.

It is possible that someone may interpret this presentation of the Great Flood as a naturally occurring event, which had no relationship whatever to any divine being. This is not my intent, nor when looking at the events "through the eyes of faith," should we come to that conclusion. It is true the Bible is not a history book, nor is it a scientific treatise, although it tells its story through real people and real events. Rather, it is presented for our instruction, in particular in matters relating to our relationship with God and with our fellow man. It teaches us that when we stray from the way Our Lord has instructed us to live, there will be consequences for that disobedience. It does not mean that we will be struck dead instantly. But, there will be consequences. When the Great Flood came, Noah, a man who walked with God responded to the Lord's inspiration and saved himself and his family as well as a boatload of animals. For sure, the Great Flood was a result of the order that God had imposed at the moment of Creation and all proceeded from that moment in accordance with and under the direction of His Holy Will. Those who were not in consonance with the Lord, and who derided the Lord's Word spoken by Noah, perished. They did not perish because God struck them dead on the spot. They died as a consequence of their attitude toward God and His Word, that is, their deaths were a consequence of their own sins.

WHAT OF THE FUTURE?

We can be certain that scientist will continue to make startling discoveries in the years ahead. From the information they collect, they will develop new hypotheses to explain the universe and life within it. Some old hypotheses will be cast aside because they are no longer supported by the newer data. Indeed, many of the scientific models described in this book may be superseded or significantly revised because of new discoveries. This is the nature of science and so it should be.

But, what does this mean for the person of faith as he or she hears of each new discovery supplanting years of consensus within the scientific community? My first answer to this question would be, "Fear not." For centuries, persons of faith have wrestled with these issues. St. Thomas Aquinas wrestled with these issues in the thirteenth century, always finding consistency with his faith in God. Teilhard de Chardin was a Jesuit priest who studied and practiced geology and paleontology in the field in the first half of the twentieth century. His absolute faith in God and God's unique role in creation never wavered in pursuit of his scientific endeavors. Seeing the world we live in "through the eyes of faith" was not a contradiction in his eyes. Just as these men have been able to see the hand of God and the discoveries of science as evidence of the one world we live in, a world of God's creation and a world of man's discovery, we too should ponder the wonders of science in the light of our faith.

Consider two possible scientific discoveries that would be breathtaking and monumental in the world of scientific investigation to ponder how we might see them "through the eyes of faith." Think about a possible discovery of life somewhere else in the universe. Second, consider the possibility of scientific proof of one or more parallel universes. Let us consider how we might reconcile these two possible discoveries by looking at them through the eyes of faith. However, we must first have patience to allow the discoveries to be reviewed and repeated numerous times before we leap to conclusions. Many startling discoveries have been made raising the excitement of scientific communities to a fever pitch, only to be later withdrawn when it was discovered that the experiments could not be repeated or that the data had been corrupted. Indeed, in some cases, including the infamous discovery of the Piltdown Man, thought to be a missing link between man and apes, there is simply fraud in the perpetuation of an elaborate hoax.

Alien life

Reputable scientists, including scientists at NASA, spend a great deal of money and effort trying to discover extraterrestrial life. Some of that work is conducted firmly rooted in the ground of mother Earth by analyzing electromagnetic energy emanating from space for evidence of intelligent life, known in the world of government acronyms as SETI, Search for Extraterrestrial Intelligence. The Arecibo Telescope in Puerto Rico depicted in Figure 92 is a part time participant in the program.[237] Plans have been announced to build a radio telescopic array dedicated to the search for Extraterrestrial Intelligence. This program, estimated to cost $26 million dollars will be dedicated to full time to the Search for Extraterrestrial Intelligence program.

Figure 92 Arecibo Telescope

One of the major objectives of the two Viking missions to Mars was to search for evidence of extraterrestrial life.[238] Indeed, it is probably safe to say that every space mission involving a landing has, as part of its mission, the search for extraterrestrial life.

The Voyager interstellar probe has a greeting in fifty five languages from Earth, as well as recordings of typical Earth sounds and photographs of typical Earth scenes all directed toward any extraterrestrial intelligent life that may encounter it.[239] Not everyone thinks that describing the beauty of Earth is a particularly wise idea. Stephen Hawking, in particular has issued a fairly sobering warning:

> We only have to look at ourselves to see how intelligent life might develop into something we wouldn't want to meet. I imagine they might exist in massive ships, having used up all the resources from their home planet. Such advanced aliens would perhaps become nomads, looking to conquer and colonize whatever planets they can reach.

He concludes that trying to make contact with alien races is "a little too risky." He said,

> If aliens ever visit us, I think the outcome would be much as when Christopher Columbus first landed in America, which didn't turn out very well for the Native Americans.[240]

Suppose that at some time in the future, life is discovered somewhere else in the cosmos. Is this inevitably a world-shattering event for the man of faith? Again, I say, "Fear not." For the man of faith, such a discovery would mean that, in His omnipotence, God chose to create life in other places because it pleased Him to do so; God's power has never been limited to Earth.

A similar question could be posed to the secular man. Suppose that in the future a planet is discovered that is very nearly like Earth in every significant respect except that it is completely devoid of life, either past or present. Would this mean to the secular man that life could exist only on Earth and nowhere else? Even to the secular man, I would have to say, "Fear not." For a man of faith, it would mean that God chose not to create life in that particular world, as He chose to do on Earth. It would, however, create a dilemma for the secular man to determine why life had not spontaneously emerged on a seemingly habitable planet.

Figure 93 Viking lander on Mars

Parallel Universes

The concept of parallel universes existing within our own universe is a commonly used theme in the genre of science fiction. Often, it includes exactly the same people living different lives, usually evil, as people in our universe. Because of some quirk in the "space time continuum," the characters are able to move into the parallel universe where they inevitably encounter themselves as their parallel evil twin. Now this might all be just fun science fiction, except that some scientists have espoused hypotheses about the potential existence of real parallel universes. Not too long ago, the History channel devoted one of its *The Universe* presentations to the examination of the concept of parallel universes. Sometimes they are referred to as other dimensions. Stephen Hawking has presented concepts supported by mathematical analyses hypothesizing the possibility of these additional dimensions. He provides a concise summary of his these concepts in *The Universe in a Nutshell*:

> As an example of the power of the anthropic principle, consider the number of dimensions in space. It is a matter of common experience that we live in three dimensional space. That is to say, we can represent the position of a point in space by three numbers, for example, latitude, longitude, and height above sea level. But why is space three dimensional? Why isn't it two, or four, or some other number of dimensions, as in science fiction? In M-theory, space has nine or ten dimensions, but it is thought that six or seven of the dimensions are curled up very small, leaving three dimensions that are large and nearly flat.[241]

Ponder this concept for a few moments in the light of all we have been taught about angels and their ability to watch over us, guide us, and protect us. Indeed, once again it calls to mind the age-old question, "How many angels can dance on the head of a pin?" Assuming angels exist in one or more of these curled up dimensions, the answer is again: as many as necessary to fulfill God's will.

That answer is also consistent from the scientific view. Since angels are pure spirit, they have no mass. Without mass, they are not bound by the Exclusionary Principle—that two objects cannot occupy the same space at the same time. The angels dancing on a pin argument may seem frivolous; however, it undergirds the concept that Heaven, Hell, Purgatory, and any other spiritual states have no need to be physically large at all. Indeed, by definition they are spiritual, not physical.

The concept of parallel universes or dimensions is not some fanciful idea confined to the realm of wild haired theorists. Practical measures are being taken to investigate the possibility of their existence. NASA is conducting experiments to prove the existence of parallel universes. Dr. Sam Ting, Nobel laureate in physics, the principle investigator had this to say about NASA objectives of the Alpha Magnetic Spectrometer-2 (AMS):

> One of his desires is that the particles recorded by AMS prove the existence of a parallel universe made up of anti-matter, or particles that are, in electrical charge and magnetic properties, the exact opposite of regular particles. Such a universe has been theorized, but not proven. The discovery of massive amounts of anti-matter could answer fundamental questions about the universe's origin.[242]

One of the common concepts of parallel universes is that they do not follow the universal laws of science that we live under and readily accept. Physical boundaries in one universe may not affect beings in a parallel universe. Similarly, the laws of gravity and the transmission of light may be different or entirely absent. It is also important to recognize that these hypotheses do not suppose a universe that is millions of light years away or even outside our own universe. Rather, a parallel universe is deemed to coexist within our own universe. One common assumption seems to be that, other than for purposes of science fiction, there appears no means of moving between such universes or dimensions. This assumption does not stop scientists from seeking to find ways to discover, examine, or measure matter and events in parallel universes.

The question for our purposes is: "What would a successful discovery of a parallel universe mean to a man of faith?" Once again, I say, "Fear not." I say this because I think this is a classic case of the language barrier between the secular man and the man of faith. Specifically, I think the Bible is replete with examples of parallel universes and the differing laws of behavior that apply. However, we do not usually think about them as parallel universes because we use different names for them. Nevertheless, the Biblical parallel universes share many of the characteristics anticipated by serious scientists in their search for such things. Allow me to name a few, and then I will proceed to consider how these might fit the definition of parallel universes even if they do not conform to the norm in science fiction in which one encounters one's evil twin. Ponder the following as parallel universes:

- Heaven
- Hell
- Sheol or the Netherworld
- Purgatory

Since I am only attempting to characterize the spiritual realms as consistent with ideas concerning parallel universes, and not attempting to present a theological treatise on the teachings of the Church, I will address only Heaven and Hell in this context. The mental exercise of defining the laws of the other parallel universe is left to the reader.

Beginning with heaven, the Catechism of the Catholic Church defines heaven as follows:

> 1023 Those who die in God's grace and friendship and are perfectly purified live forever with Christ. They are like God for ever, for they "see him as he is," face to face.
>
> By virtue of our apostolic authority, we define the following: According to the general disposition of God, the souls of all the saints...and other faithful who died after receiving Christ's holy Baptism (provided they were not in need of purification when they died...or, if they then did need or will need some purification, when they have been purified after death...) already before they take up their bodies again and before the general judgment—and this since the Ascension of our Lord and Savior Jesus Christ into heaven—have been, are and will be in heaven, in the heavenly Kingdom and celestial paradise with Christ, joined to the company of the holy angels. Since the Passion and death of our Lord Jesus Christ, these souls have seen and do see the divine essence with an intuitive vision, and even face to face, without the mediation of any creature.[243]
>
> 1024 This perfect life with the Most Holy Trinity—this communion of life and love with the Trinity, with the Virgin Mary, the angels and all the blessed—is called "heaven." Heaven is the ultimate end and fulfillment of the deepest human longings, the state of supreme, definitive happiness.[244]

You may notice that Heaven is not really defined as a place. One in Heaven "sees God," "shares a communion of life," and is in a "state of supreme, definitive happiness." Nevertheless, using other words, Heaven could certainly meet a definition of a parallel universe and it would clearly have differing laws of physical behavior. With the exception of a very small number of cases described in the Bible and in Church Tradition, for example, Our Lord Jesus Christ, The Blessed Virgin Mary, and Elijah, at this time everyone in Heaven is pure spirit. Only at the General Judgment will the saints in Heaven rejoin their new, glorified bodies. Although the saints are pure spirit, they retain their identities, personalities, and names.

> 1025 To live in heaven is "to be with Christ." the elect live "in Christ," but they retain, or rather find, their true identity, their own name.[245]

These definitions and descriptions give us some idea of the nature of the laws that govern those present in Heaven. One such law is that those in the parallel universe of Heaven can see into and hear the activities of those still residing in our universe on Earth. It something like a two-way mirror; they can see and hear us, but we cannot see or hear them unless they choose to communicate with us or reveal themselves to us. The most common revelation of this characteristic is the actions of angels, previously defined in Catechism reference 1024, above. Let's look at some familiar examples. The angel Gabriel revealed himself to the Blessed Virgin Mary and communicated with her in an ordinary sense.

> **In the sixth month, the angel Gabriel was sent from God to a town of Galilee called Nazareth, to a virgin betrothed to a man named Joseph, of the house of David, and the virgin's name was Mary. And coming to her, he said, "Hail, favored one! The Lord is with you." But she was greatly troubled at what was said and pondered what sort of greeting this might be.**

Figure 94 The Annunciation

Luke 1:26-29.

The saints in Heaven can see us and hear us. They are aware of the things that we do and the decisions we make in our lives. When those decisions lead us to communion with God, and especially a return to faith and repentance for sin, there is great joy in Heaven.

> **I tell you, in just the same way there will be more joy in heaven over one sinner who repents than over ninety-nine righteous people who have no need of repentance.**

Luke 15:7.

One of the elements of the Catholic faith is a belief in the "communion of saints." Among other things, it means that in our daily lives in our universe on Earth, we can ask them for intercessory prayer on our behalf and the saints in heaven can hear us. Of course, Our Blessed Mother, as the Mother of God enjoys a special role as intercessor without peer.

> 956 The intercession of the saints. "Being more closely united to Christ, those who dwell in heaven fix the whole Church more firmly in holiness... They do not cease to intercede with the Father for us, as they proffer the merits which they acquired on earth through the one mediator between God and men, Christ Jesus... So by their fraternal concern is our weakness greatly helped. [246]

Figure 95 Guardian angel

One of the implications of this belief is that those in Heaven are not confined by physical space as we are. I can ask St. Margaret of Scotland (one of my wife's ancestors) to pray for me. At the same time, my daughter who is living in Kansas at this time can also ask St. Margaret to pray for her and she will hear both of our prayers, even though my daughter and I are separated by hundreds of miles. In essence, one of the laws of Heaven is omnipresence. The communion of saints as a confluence of Heaven and Earth is beautifully depicted in the fresco, *La Disputa del Sacramento*, by Raphael in the Apostolic Palace in the Vatican.

Hell apparently has some differing characteristics as a place for beings of pure spirit. *The Catechism of the Catholic Church* defines Hell, principally, as a separation from God.

> 1033 We cannot be united with God unless we freely choose to love him. But we cannot love God if we sin gravely against him, against our neighbor or against ourselves: "He who does not love remains in death. Anyone who hates his brother is a murderer, and you know that no murderer has eternal life abiding in him. Our Lord warns us that we shall be separated from him if we fail to meet the serious needs of the poor and the little ones who are his brethren. To die in mortal sin without repenting and accepting God's merciful love means remaining separated from him forever by our own free choice. This state of definitive self-exclusion from communion with God and the blessed is called "hell."[247]
>
> 1035 The teaching of the Church affirms the existence of hell and its eternity. Immediately after death the souls of those who die in a state of mortal sin descend into hell, where they suffer the punishments of hell, "eternal fire." The chief punishment of hell is eternal separation from God, in whom alone man can possess the life and happiness for which he was created and for which he longs.[248]

As in heaven, we retain our consciousness, personality, and name in Hell. We are aware of our condition and we, at last, realize what we denied throughout our lives on Earth—that God loves us and wants us to be with Him, but by our ultimate rejection of Him, we are forever bound by our choice and suffer the regret of separation and lost joy.

I also think that the eternal loss of the opportunity to be in the presence of God also explains the church's teaching that "The chief punishment of hell is eternal separation from God" from Catechism reference 1035. The general perception, at least in common media portrayal of hell, when not being derided as a fiction concocted to scare little children into improved behavior, is one of pools of fire with long tailed devils poking at the pitiful residents of hell with pitchforks. I think a better description that applies the Catechism teaching on the principle punishment as a separation from God has to do with our own personal wants and desires. Certainly, we have all heard the phrase, "a burning desire" indicating a desire so great that it almost consumes us like fire. I think the story of the disciples' encounter with Jesus on the road to Emmaus captures that idea of "burning desire." During most of the

Figure 96 La Disputa del Sacramento

time of their encounter with Jesus, they were precluded from recognizing Him, even while He was opening the Scriptures to them.

> **Then beginning with Moses and all the prophets, he interpreted to them what referred to him in all the scriptures.**

Luke 24:27.

Finally, at the breaking of the bread they recognized Him only to have Him vanish from their sight.

> **And it happened that, while he was with them at table, he took bread, said the blessing, broke it, and gave it to them. With that their eyes were opened and they recognized him, but he vanished from their sight.**

Luke 24:30-31.

But, all the time they were with Him, they did not recognize Him because they thought He was still dead and buried in the tomb in Jerusalem. Because of their intense desire to be with Jesus, yet thinking that that was forever out of their reach because of His death, they were consumed with an insatiable burning desire. I think that is what they mean in the following verse.

> **Then they said to each other, "Were not our hearts burning (within us) while he spoke to us on the way and**

Figure 97 Pilgrims on the Road to Emmaus

opened the scriptures to us?"
Luke 24:32.

Their burning hearts were relieved by their faith and their assurance that He had risen indeed and they would never be separated from Him again. Contrast that feeling with those who have deliberately rejected God throughout their lives, and because they died in mortal sin, rejecting God's forgiving Grace, must for all eternity live with their self-imposed separation from God. Now the truth before them can no longer be denied. Their hearts will burn within them forevermore and there is no reprieve, no pardon. This separation from God called by the Catechism the principal punishment of hell is, at the same time, an all-consuming punishment of fire; the burning desire to be with God, forever denied.

Figure 98 Dives and Lazarus

Although those in Hell may have a view of heaven, they are denied the communication available by the saints and angels in Heaven with those living on Earth. We see these characteristics in a parable presented by Our Lord in the Gospel St. Luke, commonly called the parable of Dives and Lazarus.

When the poor man died, he was carried away by angels to the bosom of Abraham. The rich man also died and was buried, and from the netherworld, where he was in torment, he raised his eyes and saw Abraham far off and Lazarus at his side..."Moreover, between us and you a great chasm is established to prevent anyone from crossing who might wish to go from our side to yours or from your side to ours." He said, "Then I beg you, father, send him to my father's house, for I have five brothers, so that he may warn them, lest they too come to this place of torment." But Abraham replied, "They have Moses and the prophets. Let them listen to them." He said, "Oh no, father Abraham, but if someone from the dead goes to them, they will repent." Then Abraham said, "If they will not listen to Moses and the prophets, neither will they be persuaded if someone should rise from the dead."

Luke 16:22-23, 26-31.

In the parable we see the rich man in hell, here called the netherworld, and the Lazarus in Heaven, the bosom of Abraham. More importantly, the rich man can see Lazarus enjoying the blissful existence of heaven. However, the laws of these two parallel universes are such that those in either universe cannot cross over to the other:

> **Moreover, between us and you a great chasm is established to prevent anyone from crossing who might wish to go from our side to yours or from your side to ours.**

Luke 16:26.

We also see the prohibition of those in Hell communicating with those in our universe on Earth.

> **If they will not listen to Moses and the prophets, neither will they be persuaded if someone should rise from the dead.**

Luke 16:26.

We shall so see that the converse does not hold, that is, those in heaven are permitted to communicate with, and become visible to those in our universe on Earth. This is particularly true of angels. Indeed, this is their principle mission and reason for existence. However, there are also instances of others in heaven appearing and communicating with those in our earthly universe, such as the appearance of Elijah and Moses appearing to our Lord and two of His apostles at the Transfiguration. We shall look at a few examples of this from the Scriptures and the Tradition of the Catholic Church, but we shall by no means exhaust the examples.

> **The LORD appeared to Abraham by the terebinth of Mamre, as he sat in the entrance of his tent, while the day was growing hot. Looking up, he saw three men standing nearby.**

Genesis 18:1-2.

> **While the two men walked on farther toward Sodom, the LORD remained standing before Abraham.**

Genesis 18:22.

Here we see God Himself making an appearance and conversing with Abraham. Of

Figure 99 The Transfiguration

course, as Creator of the heavens and the Earth, God, in His omnipotence is not bound by any law of nature. He created them according to His pleasure and can adjust them according to His will. The angels present another example of the application of the differing laws applying to each of the parallel universes.

Before addressing the implications of angelic actions on the laws of universes, let us pause to consider the teachings of the Catholic Church regarding angels.

One very useful source is the writings of St. Augustine and the Catechism of the Catholic Church:

> 329 St. Augustine says: "'Angel' is the name of their office, not of their nature. If you seek the name of their nature, it is 'spirit'; if you seek the name of their office, it is 'angel': from what they are, 'spirit', from what they do, 'angel.' "With their whole beings the angels are servants and messengers of God. Because they "always behold the face of my Father who is in heaven" they are the "mighty ones who do his word, hearkening to the voice of his word".[249]
>
> 330 As purely spiritual creatures angels have intelligence and will: they are personal and immortal creatures, surpassing in perfection all visible creatures, as the splendor of their glory bears witness.[250]

Here we learn a number of things about angels. They are spiritual creatures. Recalling our discussion of the creation of man, this was the indelible mark which set man apart from all of the other living creatures of the Earth. This was the image of God, the very essence of God Himself from which personality, our memories, our intelligence, our reason, our spiritual immortality are derived.

In the story of Abraham encountering the Lord and the two angels, en route to Sodom, we see angels appearing like men to Abraham and to Lot. Thus angels are able to enter our earthly universe and appear like men to us. That ability is apparently purely optional to them, as we see in the incident with the prophet Elisha.

> **Early the next morning, when the attendant of the man of God arose and went out, he saw the force with its horses and chariots surrounding the city. "Alas!" he said to Elisha.**

Figure 100 Abraham before God and the Angels

"What shall we do, my lord?" "Do not be afraid," Elisha answered. "Our side outnumbers theirs." Then he prayed, "O LORD, open his eyes, that he may see." And the LORD opened the eyes of the servant, so that he saw the mountainside filled with horses and fiery chariots around Elisha.

2 Kings 6:15-17.

Figure 101 Elisha and the Heavenly Host

The appearance of the fiery chariots is clearly meant to indicate an angelic host sent by God to protect the prophet Elisha. For the purposes of understanding the concepts of parallel universes, we can understand that the angelic host, that is an army of purely spiritual beings, was present though invisible to all but the prophet Elisha, who could see them "through the eyes of faith." By the will of God, they became visible to Elisha's attendant.

In the story of St. Peter's imprisonment we can see the ability of angels to converse with human beings in our universe and even make physical contact with us. We can also see that angels are not bound by the physical constraints that constrain us, such as the walls of buildings. Indeed, not only are they not constrained; they have power to manipulate physical constraints to their will as with the chains depicted in Figure 102.

On the very night before Herod was to bring him to trial, Peter, secured by double chains, was sleeping between two soldiers, while outside the door guards kept watch on the prison. Suddenly the angel of the

Figure 102 St. Peter freed from prison

> **Lord stood by him and a light shone in the cell. He tapped Peter on the side and awakened him, saying, "Get up quickly." The chains fell from his wrists.**

Acts 12:6-7.

Finally, we see in the Isaiah story the ability of angels to fly—or at least their ability not to be bound by the law of gravity. Although angels are sometimes depicted in the Bible as having wings, more often, as with Abraham's, Elisha's Isaiah's, and St. Peter's encounters with angels, there is no mention of wings.

> **Then one of the seraphim flew to me, holding an ember which he had taken with tongs from the altar. He touched my mouth with it. "See," he said, "now that this has touched your lips, your wickedness is removed, your sin purged."**

Isaiah 6:6-7.

As I described before, I have had personal corroboration of spiritual beings unconstrained by the physical laws of our universe: specifically, the testimony of my father during his out of body experience following his accident. In my father's experience, he was able to float over the operating room unseen by anyone present; he was able to observe what happened in that room and hear what was said; he was able to see and hear even while his body was lying on the operating table, completely unconscious in the normal sense of the word, his senses of sight and hearing completely gone as he was deeply anesthetized for the surgery. He was affected neither by gravity nor by the laws of optics. His ability to hear and see without physical sensory organs indicate conclusively to me that he was alive and cognizant in a spiritual sense, and that his abilities in this sense were precisely what could be reasonably expected in a parallel universe.

The point of this discussion is to consider what such a discovery in the world of science would mean to a person of faith. My conclusion is that the existence of parallel universes is well within the power of God, whom we believe is omnipotent. As a matter of faith, discovery of a parallel universe should provide no cause to doubt the truth presented in the Scriptures or by Holy Mother Church. At most, it would be another example of science and religion using different terminology to discuss the same phenomena of God's awesome creation.

Figure 103 Isaiah visited by a Seraph

CONCLUSION

In conclusion, I would say to my fellow Christians and our Jewish brothers and sisters, "Hold fast to the faith that has been handed down to us over uncountable millennia and persevere to the end." By any measure, we do indeed live in the same world created by our God and explored and studied by scientists the world over. Every scientific model is nothing more than a hypothesis that has been tested and found to be supported by measurable observations. But even a hypothesis that gains a great deal of scientific consensus may yet be shown to be incompatible with newer observations and will have to be revised and discarded. Those are the rules of scientific discovery. They are not the rules of faith. In our faith, we must be humble enough to accept the teachings of God's sacred Word and the teachings of our Church. What we do not understand, we must simply accept as the work of God that is, at least for a time, beyond our comprehension. As new scientific discoveries are unveiled, we should ponder them in relation to our faith. We should seek to understand them in ways that strengthen our faith, not weaken it. Undoubtedly, at times, discoveries will be made that we cannot understand or will call into question some article of faith. In those instances, we must be patient and seek a deeper knowledge of our faith. But, we must remember that some startling announcement of a scientific discovery is not the last word in science, much less in religion. Science must retest and verify the finding and it must do so in a scientifically authentic way. It is not adequate to attempt to re-prove a hypothesis. No, it must be challenged, debated, defended and attacked in every conceivable way. Only if it withstands such intense scrutiny can our confidence in it grow. In science there is really no such thing as a consensus that must be accepted and all dissent silenced. That is politics; it has no place in science.

Recall the great consensus on luminiferous aether concerning the transmission of light that was accepted science from the time of Sir Isaac Newton to the time of Albert Einstein, a period of more than two centuries. Of course, this does not mean that we should not question our faith. If we do not question our faith, we are no longer gaining in our knowledge of God. But, as we question our faith, we must seek answers that deepen and strengthen our faith. Questions should strengthen our faith as we seek to answer them. This is the answer to the question that inspired this book, "What do we tell our children?" Look at all the discoveries of science "through the eyes of faith," realizing that the world of science is the very same world created by our God, but too often, described in different language, separating it from our lives. We must continue to seek a deeper and closer knowledge of our God and trust that someday we will understand the mysteries, in the words of Our Lord,

> **For there is nothing hidden that will not become visible, and nothing secret that will not be known and come to light.**

Luke 8:17.

Figure 104 Rembrandt's "Supper at Emmaus"
Depicting the astonishment of the faithful upon having their eyes opened to Christ

for Patty

Table of Tables

Table of Figures

Image Credits

Michele Giannetti: 14, 15, 16, 17, 18, 19, 20, 21, 46 (based on The Crucible of Creation by Prof. Simon Conway Morris), 48, 51, 52, 54, 55, 56, 62, 72, 84, 91

NASA: 26, 27, 30 (Carina Nebula (NGC3372) photographed by Hubble telescope),32 (ESA and L. Ricci (ESO), 33, 34 (Rob Simmons), 36, 36 (Chris Scotese), 38 (photograph taken by Apollo 8 astronaut Bill Anders, Christmas Eve, 1968), 92, 93

William Lynn: 9, 28, 65 (photo on display at hospital), 74, 78

James Tissot: 5 "Healing of the Royal Official's Son," 97 "Pilgrims on the Road to Emmaus"

Raphaello Sanzio: 96 "La Disputa del Sacramento" (1509), 100: "Abraham before God and the Angels" (1515)

Figure 1: Flickr post by Gun Powder

Figure 2: http://www.bible.ca/archeology/bible-archeology-exodus-route-goshen-red-sea.htm. Used with permission.

Figure 3: http://www.advancingthecurve.com/laminin-the-god-particle-the-cross-shaped-protein

Figure 7: http://www.library.usyd.edu.au/libraries/rare/modernity/newton.html

Figure 8: http://hubblesite.org/newscenter/archive/releases/2008/11/video/e/still/3/

Figure 10: BBC Science Photo Library
Figure 11: www.thenewatlantis.com/imgLib/20110127_TNA29JacobsPriestleylg.jpg
Figure 12: Correggio "Assumption of the Virgin" Cathedral of Parma, Italy (1526-30)
Figure 22: Gustov Jäeger "Balaam and the Angel" (1836)
Figure 23: http://www.biblicalarchaeology.org/daily/biblical-artifacts/artifacts-and-the-bible/the-tel-dan-inscription-the-first-historical-evidence-of-the-king-david-bible-story/
Figure 24: http://en.wikipedia.org/wiki/Cyrus_Cylinder
Figure 25: The Digital Dead Sea Scrolls http://dss.collections.imj.org.il/isaiah
Figure 29: Carl H. Bloch "The Last Supper" (1831)
Figure 31: http://www.futuredude.com/asteroids-are-further-apart-than-you-think/
Figure 37: "The Birth of the Universe." The Kingfisher Young People's Book of Science. Graphic by Ed Gabel
Figure 40 http://www.reasons.org/articles/earth-the-champion-dynamo
Figure 41: Lunar and Planetary Institute, www.nsf.gov
Figure 42: http://php.scripts.psu.edu/users/g/k/gkw5006/interest.htm
Figure 43: SciTechDaily. April 23, 2013. Credit: Calar Alto Observatory/Max Planck Institute for Astronomy, Heidelberg, Germany. http://scitechdaily.com/herschel-solves-mystery-of-origin-of-water-in-the-upper-atmosphere-of-jupiter/
Figure 44: SIM Project
Figure 45: U.S. Department of the Interior | U.S. Geological Survey
Figure 47: http://prehistoricearth.wikia.com/wiki/Dimetrodon. Licensed under the Creative Commons Attribution-Share Alike License 3.0
Figure 49: http://neunerweb.com/index4.html
Figure 50: MacEvoy, Bruce. Human Evolution Timeline". http://sciencebasedlife.wordpress.com/2012/01/15/the-timeline-of-human-evolution-image/
Figure 53: Pietro Novelli "Cain and Abel" (1603-1647). Galleria Nazionale d'Arte Antica Rome, Italy
Figure 57: Primate pelvic bones Jordan, David K, "Human Birth & Bipedalism." August 8, 2013. http://weber.ucsd.edu/~dkjordan/resources/clarifications/HumanBirth.html
Figure 58: Bovine pelvic bone The Primitique. April 13, 2010. http://rockinm.blogspot.com/2010/04/new-fascination.html
Figure 59: Elephant birth Still shot of Riski Business video. Presented on YouTube. Elephant Safari Park, Taro, Bali. September 9, 2009
Figure 60: Australopithecus afarensis http://www.crystalinks.com/lucy.html

Figure 61: Kodiak bear[1] http://carnivoraforum.com/topic/9458341/1/
Figure 63: http://www.myyearoffaith.com/2013/01/24/the-dead-will-hear-the-voice-of-the-son-of-god/
Figure 64: Sebastien Bourdon "Moses and the Burning Bush"
Figure 66: http://www.geol.umd.edu/~lsschlei/CoolGeologyLinks/Tectonics_Website/
Figure 67: http://www.globalwarmingart.com/wiki/File:Post-Glacial_Sea_Level_png
Figure 69: Peter Essick/Aurora./Getty Images http://science.howstuffworks.com/environmental/earth/geophysics/glacier5.htm
Figure 70: http://www.geol.umd.edu/~lsschlei/CoolGeologyLinks/Tectonics_Website/
Figure 71: Red Sea. Map/Still. Britannica Online for Kids. Web. 12 Sept. 2013
Figure 73: www.online-utility.org/image/gallery_credit.jsp?title=Caucasus
Figure 75: National Geographic and IBM's Genographic Project. http://turbotodd.wordpress.com/2011/11/02/out-of-africa-ibm-and-national-geographic-map-the-human-genography/
Figure 76: Bible History Online
Figure 77: http://ngm.nationalgeographic.com/ngm/0603/feature2/images/mp_download.2.pdf. Overlay by William Lynn.
Figure 79: http://www.freerepublic.com/focus/religion/3047113/posts
Figure 80: The Gilgamesh Cylinder Seal Gilgamesh And Enkidu, Slaying The Bull Of Heaven, www.schoyencollection.com
Figure 81: Liu, J.P., Milliman, J.D., Gao, S. and Cheng, P., 2004. Holocene development of the Yellow River's subaqueous delta, North Yellow Sea. Marine Geology, 209(1-4): 45-67.
Figure 82: http://greenhorizon.org/boktower.php
Figure 83: www.ngdc.noaa.gov/mgg/ibcm/ibcmbath.html
Figure 85: http://www.dailymail.co.uk/sciencetech/article-2167731/Britains-Atlantis-North-sea--huge-undersea-kingdom-swamped-tsunami-5-500-years-ago.html#ixzz2f7FCShID
Figure 86: Barot, Trushar. "Divers Find World's Oldest Building," /http://www.timstouse.com/EarthHistory/Lemuria/japanpyramids.htm
Figure 87: Pysics Org. Pavlopetri—The World's Oldest Known Submerged Town., October 21, 2009. Photo by Jon Henderson
Figure 88: http://www.neogaf.com/forum/showthread.php?t=335649.
Figure 89: ANOEK DE GROOT/AFP/Getty Images http://duckduckgrayduck.com/2012/08/02/guy-builds-an-exact-replica-of-noahs-ark/
Figure 90: http://www.neogaf.com/forum/showthread.php?t=335649

Figure 94: www.salvemariaregina.info/Rosary.html
Figure 95: Guardian Angel Bridge (Heiliger Schutzengel), Lindberg Printing Company, no artist given.
Figure 98: Unknown Illustrator of Petrus Comestar's Bible Historiale, 1372, http://ammaguthrie.wordpress.com/category/uncategorized/page/5/
Figure 99: Raphael "The Transfiguration" (1520)
Figure 101: http://hikmatprofetik2013.blogspot.com/2013/01/kepungan-bencana-kemampuan-menghadapi.html
Figure 102: http://www.mainlesson.com/display.php?author=steedman&book =peter
Figure 103: Giovanni Battista Tiepolo "The Calling of Isaiah" (1726-1729)
Figure 104: Rembrandt "Supper at Emmaus" (1648)

References

Barclay, William. Barclay's Daily Bible Study (NT). Bible Explorer 4.0 Computer Version. WORDsearch 2006

Bryson, Bill. *The History of Just About Everything*, Broadway Books. 2003

Catechism of the Catholic Church, Libreria Editrice Vaticana, On-line edition

Giannetti, Michele. Original illustrations copyright 2014

Goren-Inbar, Naama, et al. 2004 Evidence of Hominin Control of Fire at Gesher Benot Ya'aqov, Israel. Science 304(5671):725-727.

Hawking, Stephen. *The Illustrated A Brief History of Time, Updated and Expanded Edition. Bantam Books*. 1996

Hawking, Stephen. *The Universe in a Nutshell*. Bantam Books. 2001

New American Bible, Libreria Editrice Vaticana, United States Conference of Catholic Bishops 3211 4th Street, N.E., Washington, DC 20017-1194 (202) 541-3000 November 11, 2002 Copyright (c) by United States Conference of Catholic Bishops

Schroeder, Gerald L. *Genesis and the Big Bang*, Bantam Books. Paperback and audio editions. 1992

Schroeder, Gerald L. *The Science of God,* The Free Press. 1997

Endnotes

---

[1] Gigot, Francis. “The Bible.” The Catholic Encyclopedia. Vol. 2. New York: Robert Appleton Company, 1907. 2 Feb. 2011 <http://www.newadvent.org/cathen/02543a.htm>.

[2] Gigot, Francis. “The Bible.” The Catholic Encyclopedia. Vol. 2. New York: Robert Appleton Company, 1907. 2 Feb. 2011 <http://www.newadvent.org/cathen/02543a.htm>.

[3] *The Navarre Bible, St. Paul's Epistles to the Romans and the Galatians*, 1993, pg. 73

[4] St, Thomas Aquinas. “The Summa Theologica”, Article 3. Quoted by New Advent Catholic Encylopedia: http://www.newadvent.org/summa/1002.htm

[5] Rockefeller University Press (2008, September 15). *Laminin Builds The Neuromuscular Synapse*. ScienceDaily. Retrieved February 2, 2011, from http://www.sciencedaily.com /releases/2008/09/080915083339.htm

[6] *The Navarre Bible: The Letters of Saint Paul in the Revised Standard Version*, 1999, pp200-201

[7] New American Bible footnote to 1 Corinthians

[8] Catechism of the Catholic Church, on-line edition, Copyright © Libreria Editrice Vaticana [2003 11 06], paragraph 268

[9] *Eucharistic Prayers I-IV from the 3rd Edition of the Roman Missal, English translation, 2011*

[10] iWise Wisdom on Demand. http://www.iwise.com/C32lu

[11] “The Society of Jesus.” New Advent Catholic Encyclopedia, http://www.newadvent.org/cathen/14081a.htm

[12] Alexander, M.D., Eben. *Proof of Heaven.* Simon & Schuster. 2012. Page 51

[13] Catechism of the Catholic Church, on-line edition, Copyright © Libreria Editrice Vaticana [2003 11 06], paragraph 153.

[14] Catechism of the Catholic Church, on-line edition, Copyright © Libreria Editrice Vaticana [2003 11 06], paragraph 154

[15] Hawkin, Stephen. 1996. *The Illustrated A Brief History of Time.* Pages 15-16

[16] Newton, Sir Isaac. 1704. *Optiks.* Book III, Part 1, pg. 323

[17] Bryson, Bill. 2010. *A Short History of Nearly Everything: Special Illustrated Edition.* Pg. 19

[18] Catechism of the Catholic Church, on-line edition, Copyright © Libreria Editrice Vaticana [2003 11 06], paragraph 600.

[19] Schroeder, Gerald L. *The Science of God*, Pg 161

[20] Saint Augustine, Bishop of Hippo, *The City of God Against the Pagans.* Edited by R.W. Dyson, pp 456

[21] Hawkin, Stephen. 1996. *The Illustrated A Brief History of Time.* Page 14

[22] Schroeder, Gerald L. *The Science of God*, Pg 162

[23] Catechism of the Catholic Church, on-line edition, Copyright © Libreria Editrice Vaticana [2003 11 06], paragraph 600.

[24] Catechism of the Catholic Church, on-line edition, Copyright © Libreria Editrice Vaticana [2003 11 06], paragraph 600.

[25] Stark, Andrew. "The Wall Street Journal," "There is Always Something.", Books and Ideas, November 12, 2009.

[26] Catechism of the Catholic Church, on-line edition, Copyright © Libreria Editrice Vaticana [2003 11 06], paragraph 115.

[27] Catechism of the Catholic Church, on-line edition, Copyright © Libreria Editrice Vaticana [2003 11 06], paragraph 116.

[28] Catechism of the Catholic Church, on-line edition, Copyright © Libreria Editrice Vaticana [2003 11 06], paragraph 117.

[29] SAYCE, Early History of the Hebrews (London, 1897); cited in Howlett, James. "Biblical Chronology." The Catholic Encyclopedia. Vol. 3. New York: Robert Appleton Company, 1908. 6 Feb. 2011 <http://www.newadvent.org/cathen/03731a.htm>.

[30] Drum, Walter. "Josue (Joshua)." The Catholic Encyclopedia. Vol. 8. New York: Robert Appleton Company, 1910. 6 Feb. 2011 <http://www.newadvent.org/cathen/08524a.htm>.Study of Scripture

[31] Catechism of the Catholic Church, on-line edition, Copyright © Libreria Editrice Vaticana [2003 11 06], paragraph 1961.

[32] Catechism of the Catholic Church, on-line edition, Copyright © Libreria Editrice Vaticana [2003 11 06], paragraph 1033.

[33] HUMANI GENERIS, *Encyclical of* Pope Pius XII, *12 August 1950,* Catechism of the Catholic Church, on-line edition, Copyright © Libreria Editrice Vaticana
[2003 11 06], paragraph 36.

[34] Wisdom 7:17-22, Catechism of the Catholic Church, on-line edition, Copyright © Libreria Editrice Vaticana [2003 11 06], paragraph 283.

[35] Schönborn, Christof Cardinal. "In the Beginning God Created...," St. Stephan's Cathedral, Vienna. November 13, 2005

[36] New Advent Catholic Encyclopedia, "Symbolism." http://www.newadvent.org/cathen/14373b.htm

[37] New Advent Catholic Encyclopedia, "Symbolism." http://www.newadvent.org/cathen/14373b.htm

[38] New Advent Catholic Encyclopedia, "Symbolism." http://www.newadvent.org/cathen/14373b.htm

[39] New Advent Catholic Encyclopedia, "Symbolism." http://www.newadvent.org/cathen/14373b.htm

[40] *The Ignatius Catholic Study Bible, New Testament.* Commentary on Luke 4:2, Pg 446.

[41] The Ignatius Catholic Study Bible, New Testament. Commentary on Luke 4:2 and Acts 9:1-19), Pp 446, 719.

[42] Schroeder, Gerald L. The Science of God, Pg 7

[43] Schroeder, Gerald L. The Science of God, Pg 54

[44] Schroeder, Gerald L. The Science of God, Pg 68

[45] Hawking, Stephen, *The Universe in a Nutshell,* Pg 205

[46] Schroeder, Gerald L. *The Science of God*, Pg 66

[47] Schroeder, Gerald L. *The Science of God*, Pg 54

[48] Schroeder, Gerald L. *The Science of God*, Pg 56, 65

[49] Schroeder, Gerald L. *The Science of God*, Pg 57

[50] Schroeder, Gerald L. *The Science of God*, Pg 57

[51] Schroeder, Gerald L. *The Science of God*, Pg 17

[52] Schroeder, Gerald L. *The Science of God*, Pg 17

[53] Schroeder, Gerald L. *The Science of God*, Pg 43

[54] Schroeder, Gerald L. *Genesis and the Big Bang*, Pg 23

[55] Hawking, Stephen. 1996. *The Illustrated A Brief History of Time.* Pg 138

[56] Hawking, Stephen, *The Universe in a Nutshell*, From figure 6.7. Pg 168-169

[57] Schroeder, Gerald L. *Genesis and the Big Bang*, Pg 58

[58] Schroeder, Gerald L. *The Science of God*, Pg 179

[59] Schroeder, Gerald L. *The Science of God*, Pg 29

[60] Schroeder, Gerald L. *The Science of God*, Pg 204

[61] Bryson, Bill. 2010. *A Short History of Nearly Everything.* Pg 297

[62] Schroeder, Gerald L. *The Science of God*, Pg 69

[63] Schroeder, Gerald L. *The Science of God*, Pg 94

[64] Schroeder, Gerald L. *The Science of God*, Pg 69-70

[65] Claiborne, Robert, *The Emergence of Man, The Birth of Writing.* Time Life Books,. 1974. Pg. 20.

[66] http://en.wikipedia.org/wiki/Dead_Sea_Scrolls

[67] http://en.wikipedia.org/wiki/Paleo-Hebrew—cite_ref-0

[68] Hahn, Scott. *Understanding the Scriptures: A Complete Course on Bible Study.* Midwest Theological Forum. 2008. Pg. 35.

[69] Hahn, Scott. *Understanding the Scriptures: A Complete Course on Bible Study.* Midwest Theological Forum.

2008. Pgs. 34-35.

[70] Laux, Fr. John. *Introduction to the Bible.* Tan Books and Publishers, Inc. 1990. Pg. 34.

[71] Hahn, Scott. *Understanding the Scriptures: A Complete Course on Bible Study.* Midwest Theological Forum. 2008. Pg. 320.

[72] Barclay, William. *Barclay's Daily Bible Study, The Gospel of Matthew, Volume 1.* Westminster Press, Philadelphia, 1958. Pp 2-3

[73] Faculty of Theology of the University of Navarre. The Navarre Bible, Joshua—Kings. 2008. Pg. 211

[74] Hahn, Scott, Ph.D. Understanding The Scriptures. 2008. Pp.36-37.

[75] Amihai Mazar, "The Spade and the Text: The Interaction Between Archeology and Israelite History Relating to the Tenth—Ninth Centuries B.C.E.," Proceedings of the British Academy 143 (The British Academy, 2007), pp. 143-144. As quoted in Biblical Archaeology Review, March/April 2013, pg.20.

[76] Catechism of the Catholic Church, on-line edition, Copyright © Libreria Editrice Vaticana [2003 11 06], paragraph 110.

[77] Hahn, Scott, Ph.D. Understanding The Scriptures. 2008. Pg.8.

[78] Schroeder, Gerald L. *The Science of God*, Pg 18

[79] Based on "*Issue 200: Ten Top Discoveries.*" *Biblical Archaeology Review*, Jul/Aug Sep/Oct 2009, pp.74-96 http://www.biblicalarchaeology.org/daily/biblical-artifacts/artifacts-and-the-bible/the-tel-dan-inscription-the-first-historical-evidence-of-the-king-david-bible-story/

[80] http://en.wikipedia.org/wiki/Cyrus_Cylinder

[81] http://debate.org.uk/topics/history/bib-qur/bibmanu.htm. (taken from McDowell. *Evidence that Demands a Verdict.* 1972:42, & Bruce 1943:16-17)

[82] http://debate.org.uk/topics/history/bib-qur/bibmanu.htm. (taken from McDowell *Evidence that Demands a Verdict.* 1972:42, & Bruce 1943:16-17)

[83] http://debate.org.uk/topics/history/bib-qur/bibmanu.htm. (taken from McDowell *Evidence that Demands a Verdict.* 1972:42)

[84] "The Bible's Manuscript Evidence" http://debate.org.uk/topics/history/bib-qur/bibmanu.htm

[85] http://en.wikipedia.org/wiki/Magdalen_papyrus

[86] Williams, Jimmy. "are the biblical Documents Reliable? *http://www.leaderu.com/orgs/probe/docs/bib-docu.html*

[87] https://www.biblicaltraining.org/library/bodmer-papyri-john

[88] Kenyon, Frederic G. *The Chester Beatty biblical Papyri Descriptions and Texts of Twelve Manuscripts on Papyrus of the Greek Bible.* 1933. http://www.bible.com.ua/lib/files/411.pdf

[89] "Diatessaron Of Tatian". http://www.documentacatholicaomnia.eu/03d/0112-

0185,_Tatianus_Syriacus,_Diatesseron_[Schaff],_EN.pdf

[90] http://en.wikipedia.org/wiki/Codex_Vaticanus

[91] http://codexsinaiticus.org/en/codex/

[92] http://en.wikipedia.org/wiki/Codex_Alexandrinus

[93] "The Bible's Manuscript Evidence" http://debate.org.uk/topics/history/bib-qur/bibmanu.htm. (taken from McDowell. *Evidence that Demands a Verdict*. (1972:50-51; 1990:48)

[94] "The Bible's Manuscript Evidence" http://debate.org.uk/topics/history/bib-qur/bibmanu.htm

[95] "The Bible's Manuscript Evidence" http://debate.org.uk/topics/history/bib-qur/bibmanu.htm

[96] Barclay, William. *Barclay's Daily Bible Study*. Commentary on Matthew 5:17-20.

[97] *http://www.gospeloutreach.net/bible.html* from: Ramm, Bernard. "Can I Trust My Old Testament?" The Kings Business, Feb., 1949 pp. 230, 231.

[98] http://www.gospeloutreach.net/bible.html

[99] http://www.gospeloutreach.net/bible.html

[100] http://www.gospeloutreach.net/bible.html from: Glueck, Nelson. "Rivers in the Desert: History of Negev." Jewish Publication Society of America, Philadelphia, 1969, p. 176.

[101] *http://www.gospeloutreach.net/bible.html* from: Albright, William Foxwell. "Archaeology and the Religions of Israel". Johns Hopkins University Press, Baltimore, 1956, p. 176.

[102] Hawking, Stephen, *The Illustrated A Brief History of Time*, pp 13-14

[103] Eliot, T.S. "The Hollow Men," quoted by Wikipedia, The Free Encylopedia. http://en.wikipedia.org/wiki/The_Hollow_Men

[104] Hawking, Stephen, *The Illustrated A Brief History of Time*, pg 61

[105] Catechism of the Catholic Church (On-line edition: http://www.vatican.va/archive/ENG0015), Paragraph 296

[106] Resnick, Robert and Halliday, David, *Physics for Students of Science and Engineering*. pg. 147

[107] Catechism of the Catholic Church (On-line edition: http://www.vatican.va/archive/ENG0015), Paragraph 338

[108] Resnick, Robert and Halliday, David, *Physics for students of Science and Engineering*. pg. 72

[109] Hawking, Stephen, *The Illustrated A Brief History of Time*, Pg 14

[110] Hawking, Stephen, *The Illustrated A Brief History of Time*, Pg 62

[111] Hawking, Stephen, *The Illustrated A Brief History of Time*, Pg 32.

[112] Bryson, Bill, *A Short History of Nearly Everything*. Pg.10.

[113] Schroeder, Gerald L. *The Science of God*, Pg 7

[114] Bryson, Bill, *A Short History of Nearly Everything*. Pg 127

[115] Bryson, Bill, *A Short History of Nearly Everything*. Pg38

[116] Bryson, Bill, *A Short History of Nearly Everything.* Pg 38

[117] Bryson, Bill, *A Short History of Nearly Everything.* Pg. 38

[118] Bryson, Bill, *A Short History of Nearly Everything.* Pg 39

[119] Coffey, Jerry, Yucatan Crater

[120] Bryson, Bill, *A Short History of Nearly Everything.* Pg 248

[121] NASA/GSFC Star Child service, question for the month of October 2001.

[122] NASA image by Chris Scotese at:

[123] NASA, Solar System Exploration.
http://solarsystem.nasa.gov/planets/profile.cfm?Object=Mercury&Display=Facts

[124] New American Bible footnote to Job 26:7

[125] New American Bible introduction to the Book of Job.

[126] Goldstein, Don, *I Have a Friend Who is Jewish. Do You?* Pg 3

[127] New American Bible footnote to Job 26:10

[128] New American Bible introduction to the Book of Isaiah.

[129] Hawking, Stephen, *The Illustrated A Brief History of Time*, Pg 156

[130] Hawking, Stephen, *The Illustrated A Brief History of Time*, Pg. 59

[131] Hawking, Stephen, *The Illustrated A Brief History of Time*, Pg 155

[132] Hawking, Stephen, *The Illustrated A Brief History of Time*, Pg154

[133] Hawking, Stephen, *The Illustrated A Brief History of Time*, Pg 106

[134] Bryson, Bill, *A Short History of Nearly Everything.* Pg 292

[135] Squyres, Steven W. "Mars." World Book Online Reference Center. 2004. World Book, Inc. Squyres, Steven W. "Mars." World Book Online Reference Center. 2004. World Book, Inc.
(http://www.worldbookonline.com/wb/Article?id=ar346000.)

[136] Bryson, Bill, *A Short History of Nearly Everything.* Pg 262

[137] Bryson, Bill, *A Short History of Nearly Everything.* Pg 343

[138] Bryson, Bill, *A Short History of Nearly Everything.* Pg 219

[139] Bryson, Bill, *A Short History of Nearly Everything.* Pp 219-220

[140] Bryson, Bill, *A Short History of Nearly Everything.* Pg 246

[141] NASA web site:
http://solarsystem.nasa.gov/planets/profile.cfm?Object=Earth&Display=Facts&System=Metric

[142] NASA data. http://heasarc.nasa.gov/docs/cosmic/planets.html

[143] Schroeder, Gerald L. *The Science of God*, Pp 185-186

[144] NASA photograph of Shoemaker—Levy comet impact on Jupiter, July 1994

[145] Bryson, Bill, *A Short History of Nearly Everything.* Pg 297

[146] Bryson, Bill, *A Short History of Nearly Everything.* Pg 255

[147] Bryson, Bill, *A Short History of Nearly Everything.* Pg 255

[148] Bryson, Bill, *A Short History of Nearly Everything.* Pg 239

[149] Leake , Jonathan. The Sunday Times, "Don't Talk to Aliens, Warns Stephen Hawking." April, 25, 2010.

[150] Merraim-Webster On-line Dictionary

[151] Bryson, Bill, *A Short History of Nearly Everything.* Pg 287

[152] Bryson, Bill, *A Short History of Nearly Everything.* Pg 288

[153] Bryson, Bill, *A Short History of Nearly Everything.* Pg 288

[154] Bryson, Bill, *A Short History of Nearly Everything.* Pg 288

[155] American Museum of Natural History. http://www.amnh.org/exhibitions/past-exhibitions/human-origins/understanding-our-past/dna-comparing-humans-and-chimps

[156] Catechism of the Catholic Church (On-line edition: http://www.vatican.va/archive/ENG0015), Part 1, Section 1, Chapter 3, Article 2

[157] Catechism of the Catholic Church (On-line edition: http://www.vatican.va/archive/ENG0015), Paragraph 2270

[158] Barclay, William, The Letters to the Romans, Pg 101

[159] Barclay, William, The Letters to the Corinthians, Pg 31

[160] Barclay, William, The Letters to the Corinthians, Pg 31

[161] Schroeder, Gerald L. *The Science of God*, Pg 17

[162] Catechism of the Catholic Church, on-line edition, Copyright © Libreria Editrice Vaticana [2003 11 06], paragraph 382.

[163] Bryson, Bill, *A Short History of Nearly Everything.* Pg 292

[164] Bryson, Bill, *A Short History of Nearly Everything.* Pg 293

[165] Bryson, Bill, *A Short History of Nearly Everything.* Pg 297

[166] Bryson, Bill, *A Short History of Nearly Everything.* Pg 297

[167] Bryson, Bill, *A Short History of Nearly Everything.* Pg 297

[168] Bryson, Bill, *A Short History of Nearly Everything.* Pg 306

[169] Bryson, Bill, *A Short History of Nearly Everything.* Pg 297

[170] Bryson, Bill, *A Short History of Nearly Everything.* Pg 338

[171] Bryson, Bill, *A Short History of Nearly Everything.* Pg 292

[172] Bryson, Bill, *A Short History of Nearly Everything*. Pg 297

[173] Schopf, J.William and Klein, Cornelius, *The Proterozoic Biosphere: A Multidisciplinary Study*. Pg 473

[174] Bryson, Bill, *A Short History of Nearly Everything*. Pg 301

[175] Schroeder, Gerald L. *The Science of God*, Pg 113

[176] Bryson, Bill, *A Short History of Nearly Everything*. Pg 323

[177] Bryson, Bill, *A Short History of Nearly Everything*. Pg 338

[178] Bryson, Bill, *A Short History of Nearly Everything*. Pg 340

[179] Schroeder, Gerald L. *The Science of God*, Pg 193

[180] Bryson, Bill, *A Short History of Nearly Everything*. Pg 88

[181] Bryson, Bill, *A Short History of Nearly Everything*. Pg 337

[182] Pope Pius XII, *Humani Generis*, August 12, 1950, Para. 36

[183] Http:///www.cartage.com

[184] Zorich, Zach. "Neanderthal Genome Decoded," *Archeology*, July/August 2010. Pg36.

[185] Schroeder, Gerald L. *The Science of God*, Pg 117

[186] Catechism of the Catholic Church (On-line edition: http://www.vatican.va/archive/ENG0015), Paragraph 33

[187] Catechism of the Catholic Church, on-line edition, Copyright © Libreria Editrice Vaticana [2003 11 06], paragraph 1605.

[188] Wikipedia. List of human evolution fossils. http://en.wikipedia.org/wiki/List_of_human_evolution_fossils

[189] Catechism of the Catholic Church (On-line edition: http://www.vatican.va/archive/ENG0015), Paragraph 366

[190] Catechism of the Catholic Church (On-line edition: http://www.vatican.va/archive/ENG0015), Paragraph 1711

[191] Smith, Wesley, "Animal Welfare Versus Animal Rights," National Review, Volume LXII, Number 5, March 22, 2010, page 45

[192] Morphological and physiological adaptations—Adaptations for Bipedalism, Australopithecines: Out of the Trees—Halfway, Homo: Into the Savanna—All the Way—Human, Humans, Walking, Running, Body, and Homo http://science.jrank.org/pages/48523/Morphological-physiological-adaptations.html#ixzz0x1LCyk6Z

[193] University of California Berkeley news release, June 14, 1999, *Meat-Eating Was Essential For Human Evolution, Says UC Berkeley Anthropologist Specializing In Diet,* By Patricia McBroom, Public Affairs

[194] Catechism of the Catholic Church (On-line edition: http://www.vatican.va/archive/ENG0015), Paragraph 390

[195] Bryson, Bill, *A Short History of Nearly Everything*. Pg 447

[196] Strauss, Bob. "Agriotherium." http://dinosaurs.about.com/od/mesozoicmammals/p/Agriotherium.htm

[197] Jungers, W.L. (1988). "Lucy's length: Stature reconstruction in Australopithecus afarensis (A.L.288-1) with

implications for other small-bodied hominids". American Journal of Physical Anthropology 76 (2): 227–231.doi:10.1002/ajpa.1330760211.PMID 3137822. http://en.wikipedia.org/wiki/Lucy_(Australopithecus)

[198] James, Steven R. (1989) "Hominid use of fire in the lower and middle Pleistocene. A review of the evidence." *Current Anthropology,* vol. 30, pp. 1-26.

[199] Catechism of the Catholic Church (On-line edition: http://www.vatican.va/archive/ENG0015), Paragraph 366

[200] Catechism of the Catholic Church, on-line edition, Copyright © Libreria Editrice Vaticana [2003 11 06], paragraph 400.

[201] Catechism of the Catholic Church, on-line edition, Copyright © Libreria Editrice Vaticana [2003 11 06], paragraph 2100.

[202] Catechism of the Catholic Church, on-line edition, Copyright © Libreria Editrice Vaticana [2003 11 06], paragraph 978.

[203] Catechism of the Catholic Church, on-line edition, Copyright © Libreria Editrice Vaticana [2003 11 06], paragraph 1264.

[204] Catechism of the Catholic Church, on-line edition, Copyright © Libreria Editrice Vaticana [2003 11 06], paragraph 1022.

[205] Kreeft, Dr. Peter. Questions of Faith: The Philosophy of Religion. Banes and Noble Audio, Portable Professor Series., October 2006. Disk 3.

[206] MacAndrew, Alec. Misconceptions Around.

[207] Hotz, Robert Lee, "New Study Redraws Path of Humans," Wall Street Journal, January 28, 2011.

[208] Jarosz, Ewa. "Tidal Dynamics in the Babel Mandab Strait—a Dissertation, 1997.

[209] Hotz, Robert Lee, "New Study Redraws Path of Humans," Wall Street Journal, January 28, 2011.

[210] Shreeve, James, National Geographic, March 2006

[211] Shreeve, James, National Geographic, March 2006

[212] Shreeve, James, National Geographic, March 2006

[213] Shreeve, James, National Geographic, March 2006

[214] New American Bible, footnote to Genesis 10:2

[215] Cozzoli, Umberto (1968). I Cimmeri. Rome Italy: Arti Grafiche Citta di Castello (Roma). http://openlibrary.org/b/OL19361902M/Cimmeri..

[216] New American Bible, footnote to Genesis 10:2

[217] *The New Encyclopædia Britannica*, 15th edition—Micropædia on "Scythian", 10:576

[218] New American Bible, footnote to Genesis 10:4

[219] New American Bible, footnote to Genesis 10:6

[220] Viviano, Pauline A., Commentary on the Book of Genesis, *The Collegeville Bible Commentary*, Pg. 51

[221] Schroeder, Gerald L. *The Science of God*, Pg 142

[222] Viegas, Jennifer. Discovery News, "Neanderthals, Humans Interbred, DNA Proves," May 6, 2010

[223] Bellamy, H. S. *Moons, Myths, and Man*. Pg 111-112

[224] MLA University of Southampton (2007, August 14). Stone Age Site Surfaces After 8000 Years. ScienceDaily. Retrieved May 12, 2009, from http://www.sciencedaily.com /releases/2007/08/070805133952.htm

[225] Waugh, Rob. "Science & Tech." July 2, 2012. Updated July 3, 2012. http://www.dailymail.co.uk/sciencetech/article-2167731/Britains-Atlantis-North-sea--huge-undersea-kingdom-swamped-tsunami-5-500-years-ago.html#ixzz2f71l7dng

[226] University of Sussex, School of Life Sciences, C1119 Modern human evolution, Lecture 6, slide 23. http://en.wikipedia.org/wiki/Doggerland#cite_note-sussex-4

[227] Ibid. and Patterson, W, "Coastal Catastrophe" (paleoclimate research document), University of Saskatchewan. http://en.wikipedia.org/wiki/Doggerland#cite_note-sussex-4

[228] Ibid and Gaffney, Vincent, "Global Warming and the Lost European Country". http://en.wikipedia.org/wiki/Doggerland#cite_note-sussex-4

[229] University of Sussex, School of Life Sciences, C1119 Modern human evolution, Lecture 6, slide 23. http://en.wikipedia.org/wiki/Doggerland#cite_note-sussex-4

[230] University of Nottingham (2009, October 16). World's Oldest Submerged Town Dates Back 5,000 Years. *ScienceDaily*. Retrieved November 8, 2010, from http://www.sciencedaily.com /releases/2009/10/091016101809.htm

[231] Barot, Trushar. "Divers Find World's Oldest Building," http://www.timstouse.com/EarthHistory/Lemuria/japanpyramids.htm

[232] "La Marmotta," Robert Kunzig, *Discover*, November 2002.

[233] New American Bible footnote to Genesis 10:25.

[234] Brenton, Sir Lancelot C.L. (1986) [1851]. The Septuagint with Apocrypha: Greek and English (reprint). Peabody: Hendrickson Publishers. ISBN 0-913573-44-2.

[235] Hirsch, EG & Hyvernat, H (2002). *"The Jewish Encyclopedia: Goper-Wood"*. The Jewish Encyclopedia. Retrieved 2007-06-27. http://en.wikipedia.org/wiki/Gopher_wood#cite_note-2

[236] McGrail, Sean (2004). *Boats of the World: From the Stone Age to Medieval Times:3*. USA: Oxford University Press. ISBN 0-19-927186-0 page 251. http://en.wikipedia.org/wiki/Boat

[237] http://starchild.gsfc.nasa.gov/docs/StarChild/questions/question24.html

[238] http://nssdc.gsfc.nasa.gov/planetary/viking.html

[239] http://voyager.jpl.nasa.gov/spacecraft/index.html

[240] Leake , Jonathan. The Sunday Times, "Don't Talk to Aliens, Warns Stephen Hawking." April, 25, 2010.

[241] Hawking, Stephen, *The Universe in a Nutshell*, Pp 87-88

[242] Siceloff, Stephen. "AMS Discoveries Will Surprise, Lead Scientist Predicts," NASA website. October 25, 2010. http://www.nasa.gov/mission_pages/shuttle/behindscenes/ams_ting.html

[243] Catechism of the Catholic Church (On-line edition: http://www.vatican.va/archive/ENG0015), Paragraph 1023

[244] Catechism of the Catholic Church (On-line edition: http://www.vatican.va/archive/ENG0015), Paragraph 1024

[245] Catechism of the Catholic Church (On-line edition: http://www.vatican.va/archive/ENG0015), Paragraph 1025

[246] Catechism of the Catholic Church (On-line edition: http://www.vatican.va/archive/ENG0015), Paragraph 956

[247] Catechism of the Catholic Church (On-line edition: http://www.vatican.va/archive/ENG0015), Paragraph 1033

[248] Catechism of the Catholic Church (On-line edition: http://www.vatican.va/archive/ENG0015), Paragraph 1035

[249] Catechism of the Catholic Church (On-line edition: http://www.vatican.va/archive/ENG0015), Paragraph 329

[250] Catechism of the Catholic Church (On-line edition: http://www.vatican.va/archive/ENG0015), Paragraph 330

About the Author

WILLIAM R. LYNN is a graduate of West Point, a former Army Officer, and an engineer. For 15 years he worked for the Army Missile Command, mostly as a civilian. He lives in Tampa, FL.